GW00384404

The LITTLE BLACK BOOK *of*

Published by
Hal Leonard Europe
A Music Sales/Hal Leonard Joint Venture Company
14-15 Berners Street, London W1T 3LJ, United Kingdom.

Exclusive distributors:
Music Sales Limited
Distribution Centre
Newmarket Road, Bury St Edmunds, Suffolk IP33 3YB, United Kingdom.

Order No. HLE90004552
ISBN 978-1-78038-794-9

Edited by Adrian Hopkins.
Music arranged by Matt Cowe.
Music processed by Paul Ewers Music Design.
Cover designed by Michael Bell Design.

Printed in the EU.

www.musicsales.com

All-Time HIT SONGS

★★★★

ABC

Words & Music by Alphonso Mizell, Frederick Perren, Deke Richards & Berry Gordy

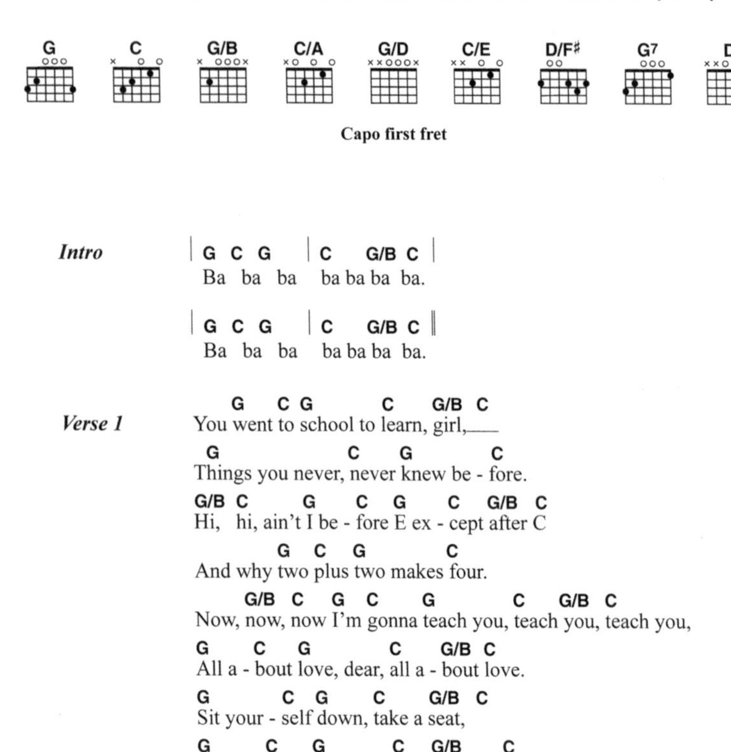

Capo first fret

```
Intro     | G  C  G    | C    G/B C |
            Ba  ba  ba    ba ba ba  ba.

          | G  C  G    | C    G/B C ||
            Ba  ba  ba    ba ba ba  ba.

               G    C G          C    G/B  C
Verse 1   You went to school to learn, girl,___
           G                  C    G           C
          Things you never, never knew be - fore.
          G/B C        G      C   G       C    G/B  C
          Hi,   hi, ain't I be - fore E ex - cept after C
                      G   C   G            C
          And why two plus two makes four.
                 G/B  C    G   C       G             C     G/B  C
          Now, now, now I'm gonna teach you, teach you, teach you,
          G      C    G          C     G/B C
          All a - bout love, dear, all a - bout love.
          G          C  G       C     G/B  C
          Sit your - self down, take a seat,
          G        C     G         C   G/B     C
          All you gotta do is re - peat after me.
```

Chorus 1

G C/A G/B C G/D C/E G C/A G/B
A, B, C, easy as one, two, three,

C G/D C/E G C/A G/B
Ah, simple as do, re, mi,

G C/A G/B G D/F♯ C/E C D G
A, B, C, one, two, three, baby, you and me girl.

G C/A G/B C G/D C/E G C/A G/B
A, B, C, easy as one, two, three,

C G/D C/E G C/A G/B
Ah, simple as do, re, mi,

C G/D C/E G D/F♯ C/E C D G
A, B, C, one, two, three, baby, you and me girl.

Bridge 1

G7
Come on, let me love you just a little bit,

Come on, let me love you just a little bit.

I'm-a gonna teach how to sing it out,

Come on, come on, come on let me show you what it's all about.

Verse 2

G C G C G/B C
Read - ing and writing a - rith - metic

G C G C
Are the branch - es of the learning tree.

G/B C G C G C G/B C
But listen, with - out the roots of love every day, girl,

G C G C
Your edu - cation ain't com - plete.

G/B C G C G C G/B C
Te - te - te - teacher's gonna show you, show you, show you,

G C G C G/B C
How to get an A, do do do do do do.

G C G C G/B C
Spell me and you, you, add the two,

G C G C G/B C
Listen to me baby, that's all you gotta do.

```
                G  C/A  G/B C  G/D C/E      G    C/A  G/B
Chorus 2     Oh, A, B,   C,     it's  easy as one, two, three,

             C  G/D  C/E         G   C/A  G/B
               Ah,  simple as do, re,   mi,

             G  C/A  G/B G   D/F♯  C/E          C   D   G
             A, B,   C,  one, two,  three, baby, you and me girl.

             G  C/A  G/B   C   G/D  C/E     G        C/A  G/B   C     G/D
             A, B,   C, it's ea - sy,   it's like count - ing  up to three,

             C/E   G     C/A  G/B    C   G/D  C/E
             Sing a sim - ple  melo - dy,

             G      D/F♯  C/E  C   D   G
             That's how  easy love can be,

             G      D/F♯  C/E  C   D   G
             That's how  easy love can be.

             G    D/F♯  C/E    C    D   G
             Sing a      simple me - lo - dy,

             G    D/F♯ C/E   C   D   G    N.C.
             One, two, three, you and me.


             N.C.
Bridge 2     Sit down girl, I think I love you,

             No, get up girl, show me what you can do.

             G      C/A  G/B       C      G/D      C/E
             Shake it,   shake it, baby,    come on now,

             G      C/A  G/B       C      G/D  C/E
             Shake it,   shake it, baby, ooh, ooh,

             G      C/A  G/B       C      G/D  C/E
             Shake it;   shake it, baby, help me.

             G    C/A   G/B   C     G/D  C/E
             One, two, three, baby, ooh, ooh,

             G   C/A  G/B  C     G/D   C/E
             A,  B,   C,   baby, now, now,

             G   C/A  G/B  C     G/D   C/E
             Do, re,  mi,  baby, now,

             G      D/F♯ C/E  C   D   G
             That's how easy love can be.
```

Chorus 3

```
G  C/A G/B   C   G/D C/E     G       C/A G/B  C     G/D
A, B,    C, it's ea - sy,   it's like count - ing   up to three,
C/E    G     C/A  G/B    C   G/D  C/E
Sing a sim - ple   melo - dy,
G       D/F♯ C/E  C    D   G7
That's how easy love can be.
```

I'm gonna teach you how to sing it out,

Come on, come on, come on let me show you what it's all about.

Chorus 4

```
G  C/A G/B   C   G/D C/E     G       C/A G/B  C     G/D
A, B,    C, it's ea - sy,   it's like count - ing   up to three,
C/E    G     C/A  G/B    C   G/D  C/E
Sing a sim - ple   melo - dy,
G       D/F♯ C/E  C    D   G7
That's how easy love can be.
```

I'm gonna teach you how to sing it out,

Sing it out, sing it out, sing it out, sing it.

Chorus 5

```
G  C/A G/B   C   G/D C/E     G       C/A G/B  C     G/D
A, B,    C, it's ea - sy,   it's like count - ing   up to three,
C/E    G     C/A  G/B    C   G/D  C/E
Sing a sim - ple   melo - dy,
G       D/F♯ C/E  C    D   G
That's how easy love can be.  To fade
```

Alone Again (Naturally)

Words & Music by Gilbert O'Sullivan

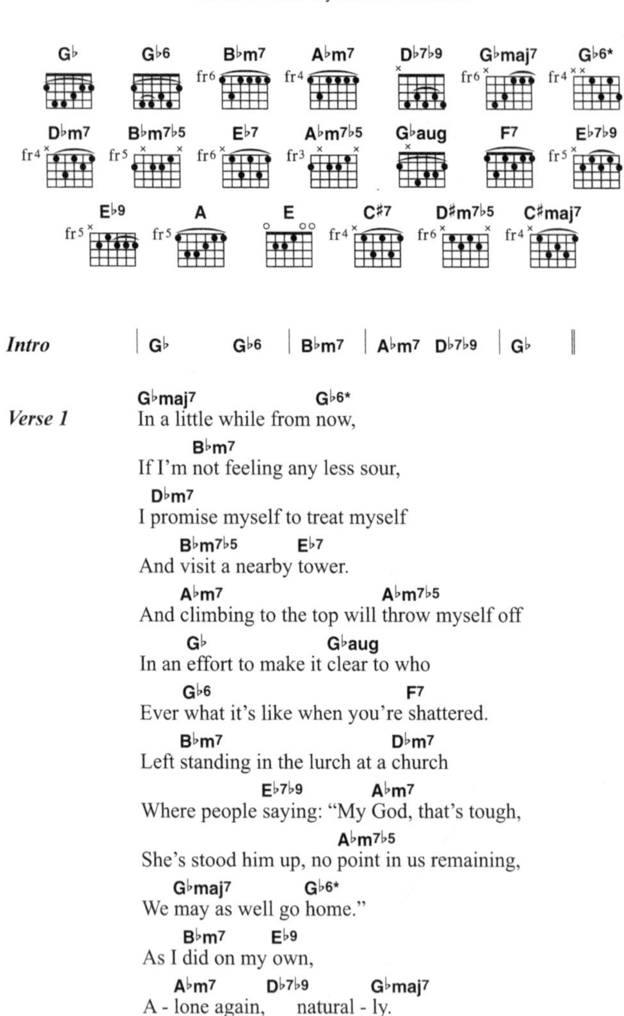

Intro | G♭ G♭6 | B♭m7 | A♭m7 D♭7♭9 | G♭ ‖

Verse 1

G♭maj7 G♭6*
In a little while from now,
B♭m7
If I'm not feeling any less sour,
D♭m7
I promise myself to treat myself
B♭m7♭5 E♭7
And visit a nearby tower.
A♭m7 A♭m7♭5
And climbing to the top will throw myself off
G♭ G♭aug
In an effort to make it clear to who
G♭6 F7
Ever what it's like when you're shattered.
B♭m7 D♭m7
Left standing in the lurch at a church
E♭7♭9 A♭m7
Where people saying: "My God, that's tough,
A♭m7♭5
She's stood him up, no point in us remaining,
G♭maj7 G♭6*
We may as well go home."
B♭m7 E♭9
As I did on my own,
A♭m7 D♭7♭9 G♭maj7
A - lone again, natural - ly.

Verse 2

```
G♭maj7                      G♭6*
To think that only yester - day
      B♭m7
I was cheerful, bright and gay.
          D♭m7
Looking forward to, well who wouldn't do,
     B♭m7♭5                E♭7♭9
The role I was about to play.
       A♭m7                         A♭m7♭5
But as if to knock me down, re - ality came around,
            G♭                  G♭aug
And with - out so much, as a mere touch
        G♭6       F7
Cut me into little pieces.
B♭m7
Leaving me to doubt,
         D♭m7                 E♭7♭9
Talk a - bout God and His mercy,
   A♭m7
Or if He really does exist,
A♭m7♭5                    G♭maj7       G♭6*
Why did He desert me    in my hour of need.
 B♭m7        E♭9
I truly am in - deed
    A♭m7       D♭7♭9       G♭maj7
A - lone again,     natural - ly.
```

Bridge

```
 A
It seems to me that there are more hearts
E                                   A♭m7♭5
Broken in the world that can't be mended
C♯7          A
   Left unat - tended.
D♯m7♭5          C♯maj7
   What do we do?
             A♭m7   D♭7
What do we do?
```

Guitar solo | G♭maj7 G♭6* | B♭m7 | D♭m7 | B♭m7♭5 E♭7 |
A♭m7	A♭m7♭5	G♭ G♭aug	G♭6 F7
B♭m7	D♭m7 E♭7♭9	A♭m7	A♭m7♭5
G♭maj7 G♭6*	B♭m7 E♭9	

A♭m7 D♭7♭9 G♭maj7
A - lone again, natural - ly.

Verse 3

G♭maj7 G♭6*
Now looking back over the years
B♭m7
And what - ever else that appears.
D♭m7
I re - member I cried when my father died,
B♭m7♭5 E♭7♭9
Never wishing to hide the tears.
A♭m7
And at sixty-five years old,
A♭m7♭5
My mother, God rest her soul,
G♭ G♭aug
Couldn't understand why the only man
G♭6 F7
She had ever loved had been taken.
B♭m7 D♭m7 E♭7♭9
Leaving her to start with a heart so badly broken,
A♭m7
De - spite encouragement from me,
A♭m7♭5
No words were ever spoken.
G♭maj7 G♭6*
And when she passed a - way,
B♭m7 E♭9
I cried and cried all day.
A♭m7 D♭7♭9 B♭m7 E♭9
A - lone again, natural - ly.
A♭m7 D♭7♭ 9 G♭maj7
A - lone again, natural - ly.

At Seventeen

Words & Music by Janis Ian

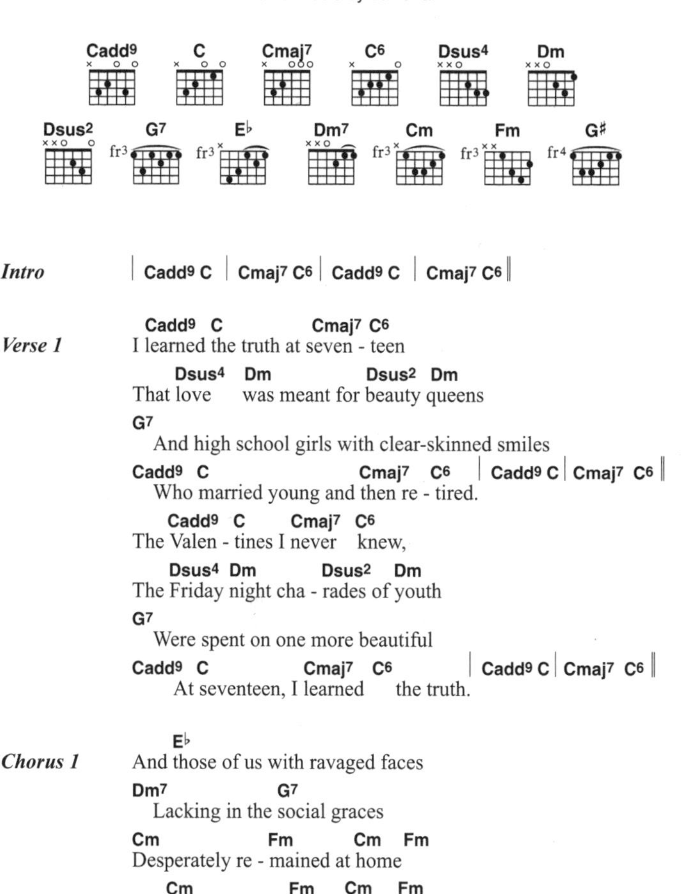

Intro

```
| Cadd9 C | Cmaj7 C6 | Cadd9 C | Cmaj7 C6 ||
```

Verse 1

```
  Cadd9  C              Cmaj7 C6
I learned the truth at seven - teen
     Dsus4   Dm              Dsus2  Dm
That love    was meant for beauty queens
G7
   And high school girls with clear-skinned smiles
Cadd9  C                     Cmaj7   C6    | Cadd9 C | Cmaj7 C6 ||
   Who married young and then re - tired.
    Cadd9  C      Cmaj7  C6
The Valen - tines I never   knew,
    Dsus4  Dm         Dsus2   Dm
The Friday night cha - rades of youth
G7
   Were spent on one more beautiful
Cadd9  C              Cmaj7   C6          | Cadd9 C | Cmaj7 C6 ||
     At seventeen, I learned     the truth.
```

Chorus 1

```
     E♭
And those of us with ravaged faces
Dm7               G7
   Lacking in the social graces
Cm                Fm        Cm   Fm
Desperately re - mained at home
    Cm            Fm     Cm    Fm
In - venting lovers on the phone
```

```
              G♯                   G7
cont.         Who called to say: "Come, dance with me,"
              Cm                 Fm        C*    Fm
                And murmured vague ob-sceni-ties.
              Dm7                    G7
                It isn't all it seems at seventeen.

                Cadd9 C            Cmaj7   C6
Verse 2       A brown eyed girl in hand me downs
              Dsus4     Dm           Dsus2      Dm
                Whose name I never could pro - nounce
              G7
                Said: "Pity please the ones who serve
              Cadd9      C               Cmaj7    C6     | Cadd9 C | Cmaj7 C6 ||
                   They only get what they de - serve,"
                       Cadd9  C          Cmaj7      C6
              And the rich re - lationed hometown queen
              Dsus4  Dm Dsus2    Dm
              Marries into what she needs
                    G7
              With a guarantee of company
                   Cadd9  C        Cmaj7 C6 | Cadd9 C | Cmaj7 C6 ||
              And haven     for the elder - ly.

                  E♭
Chorus 2      Re - member those who win the game,
              Dm7                  G7
              Lose the love they sought to gain
                 Cm              Fm
              In debentures of quality
                   Cm             Fm
              And dubious in - tegrity
                  G♯                    G7
              Their small town eyes will gape at you
                 Cm            Fm        Cm        Fm
              In dull surprise     when payment due
              G7
                Exceeds accounts received at seventeen.
```

Instrumental | Cadd9 C | Cmaj7 C6 | Dm Dsus4 | Dsus2 Dm |

| G7 | G7 | Cadd9 C | Cmaj7 C6 ||

| E♭ | E♭ | Dm7 | G7 | Cm | Fm | Cm | Fm |

| G♯ | G7 | Cm | Fm | Dm7 | Dm7 | G7 | G7 |

| Cadd9 C | Cmaj7 C6 | Cadd9 C | Cmaj7 C6 ||

Verse 3

```
 Cadd9 C         Cmaj7   C6
To those  of us who knew the pain
 Dsus4 Dm         Dsus2 Dm
Of Val - entines that ne  -  ver came,
G7
  And those whose names were never called
     Cadd9    C        Cmaj7   C6  | Cadd9 C | Cmaj7  C6 ||
When choosing sides for basket - ball
     Cadd9   C       Cmaj7 C6
It was long    ago and far a - way
   Dsus4       Dm      Dsus2    Dm
The world was younger than to - day
G7
  When dreams were all they gave for free
Cadd9   C             Cmaj7  C6      | Cadd9 C | Cmaj7  C6 ||
    To ugly duckling girls        like me.
```

Chorus 3

```
      E♭
We all play the game, and when we dare
  Dm7               G7
To cheat ourselves at solitaire
   Cm          Fm    C*    Fm
In - venting lovers on the phone
   Cm          Fm
Re - penting other lives unknown
   G♯                  G7
That call and say: "Come, dance with me,"
Cm                   Fm
  And murmur vague    obscenities
Dm7                           G7
    At ugly girls like me, at seventeen.
```

Outro | Cadd9 C | Cmaj7 C6 | Cadd9 ||

Always On My Mind

Words & Music by Wayne Thompson, Mark James and Johnny Christopher

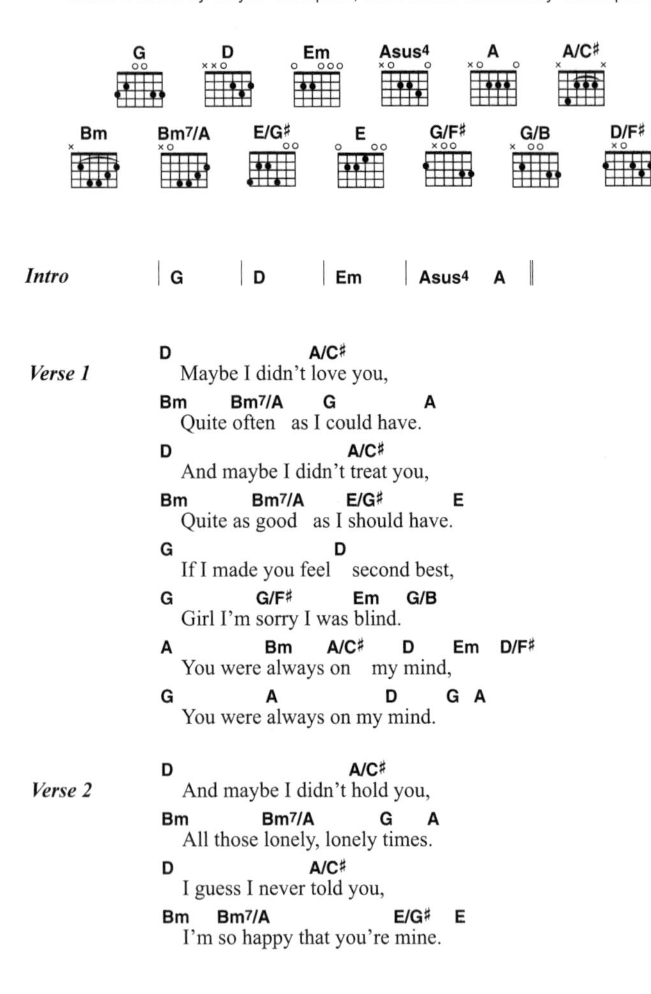

Intro | G | D | Em | Asus4 A ||

Verse 1

D A/C#
Maybe I didn't love you,
Bm Bm7/A G A
Quite often as I could have.
D A/C#
And maybe I didn't treat you,
Bm Bm7/A E/G# E
Quite as good as I should have.
G D
If I made you feel second best,
G G/F# Em G/B
Girl I'm sorry I was blind.
A Bm A/C# D Em D/F#
You were always on my mind,
G A D G A
You were always on my mind.

Verse 2

D A/C#
And maybe I didn't hold you,
Bm Bm7/A G A
All those lonely, lonely times.
D A/C#
I guess I never told you,
Bm Bm7/A E/G# E
I'm so happy that you're mine.

```
             G                              D
cont.           Little things I should have said and done,
             G       G/F#            Em    G/B
                I just never took the time.
             A            Bm    A/C#    D      Em    D/F#
                You were always on   my mind,
             G            A             D      G  A
                You were always on my mind.

             D   A/C#  Bm   Bm7/A
Middle       Tell____  me,
             G                 G/F#                Em    A
             Tell me that your sweet love hasn't died.
                 D   A/C#  Bm   Bm7/A
             And give      me,
                       G                    G/F#             Em
             Give me one more chance to keep you satis - fied,
             A                          (D)
                I'll keep you satis - fied.

Guitar solo  | D       | A/C#  A | Bm  Bm7/A | G     A |

             | D       | A/C#    | Bm  Bm7/A | E/G#  E ||

             G                              D
Verse 3         Little things I should have said and done.
             G       G/F#            Em    G/B
                I just never took the time.
             A            Bm    A/C#  D        Em    D/F#
                You were always on my mind,
             G            A             D
                You were always on my mind.

             A            Bm    A/C#    D      Em    D/F#
Outro           You were always on   my mind,
             G            A             D
                You were always on my mind.
```

Baby Love

Words & Music by Brian Holland, Lamont Dozier & Edward Holland

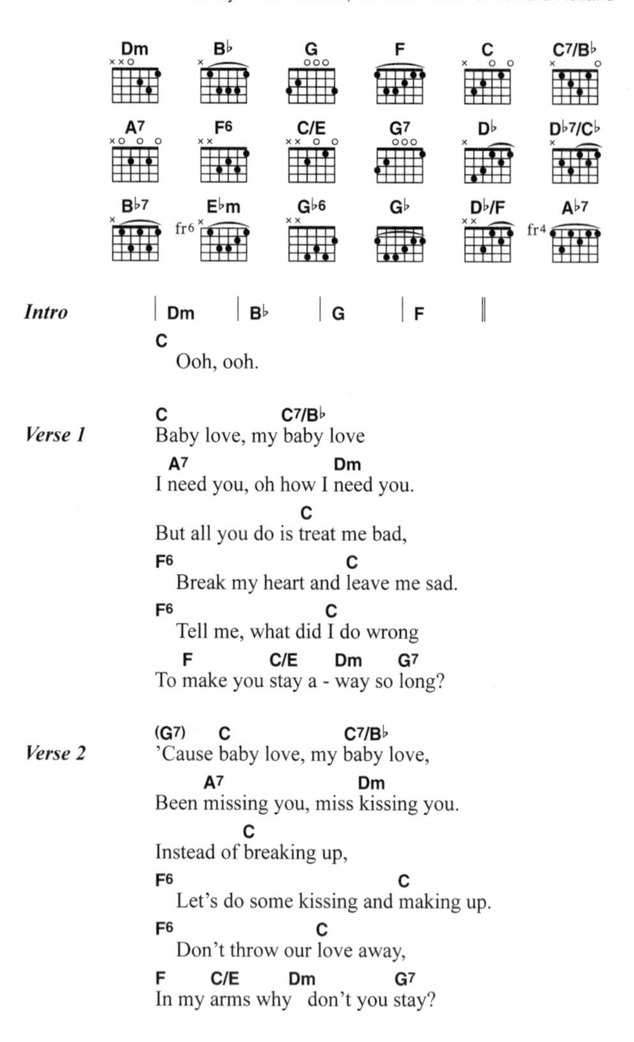

Intro | Dm | B♭ | G | F ||

C
Ooh, ooh.

Verse 1

C C7/B♭
Baby love, my baby love

A7 Dm
I need you, oh how I need you.

C
But all you do is treat me bad,

F6 C
Break my heart and leave me sad.

F6 C
Tell me, what did I do wrong

F C/E Dm G7
To make you stay a - way so long?

Verse 2

(G7) C C7/B♭
'Cause baby love, my baby love,

A7 Dm
Been missing you, miss kissing you.

C
Instead of breaking up,

F6 C
Let's do some kissing and making up.

F6 C
Don't throw our love away,

F C/E Dm G7
In my arms why don't you stay?

Verse 3

C   C7/B♭
Need you, need you,

A7   Dm
Baby love, ooh, baby love.

Instrumental

| Dm | C | F6 | C |
| F6 | C | F C/E | Dm G7 ||

Verse 4

C   C7/B♭
Baby love, my baby love,

A7   Dm
Why must we sepa - rate, my love?

C
All of my whole life through

F6   C
I never loved no one but you.

F6   C
Why you do me like you do?

F   C/E   Dm G7
I get this need.

D♭
Ooh, ooh,

Verse 5

D♭   D♭/C♭
Need to hold you once a - gain, my love,

B♭7   E♭m
Feel your warm em - brace, my love.

D♭
Don't throw our love away,

G♭6   D♭
Please don't do me this way.

G♭6   D♭
Not happy like I used to be,

G♭   D♭/F   E♭m   A♭7   (D♭)
Loneli - ness has   got the best of me.

Verse 6

D♭ D♭/C♭
My love, my baby love,

B♭7 E♭m
I need you, oh how I need you.

D♭
Why you do me like you do

G♭6 D♭
After I've been true to you?

G♭6 D♭
So deep in love with you.

G♭ D♭/F E♭m A♭7
Baby, baby, baby. Ooh,

Verse 7

(A♭7) D♭ D♭/C♭
Till it's hurting me, till it's hurting me,

B♭7 E♭m
Ooh, baby love.

G♭6 D♭
Don't throw our love away,

G♭6 D♭
Don't throw our love away. *To fade*

Bohemian Rhapsody

Words & Music by Freddie Mercury

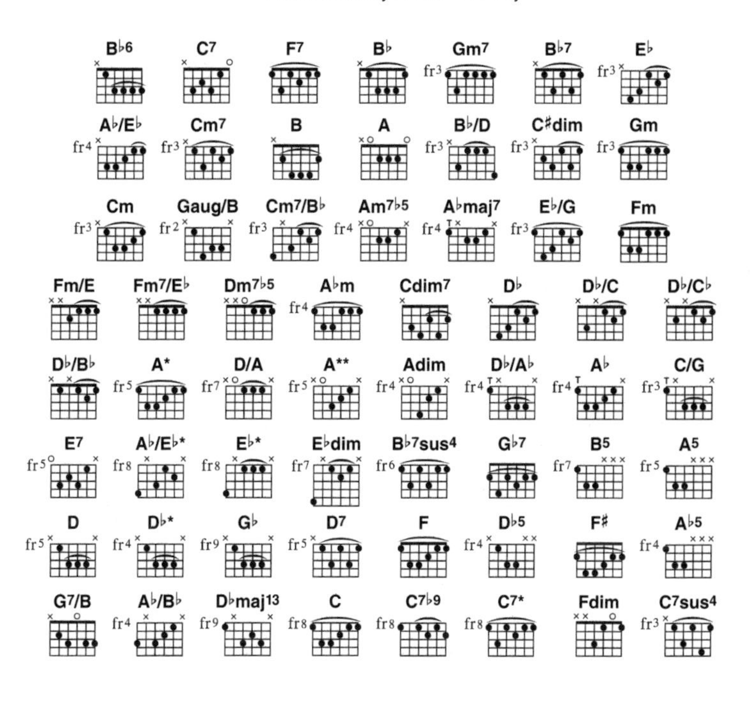

Intro

```
B♭6                          C7
Is this the real life? Is this just fantasy?
F7                                    B♭
Caught in a landslide, no es - cape from reality.
Gm7                   B♭7                         E♭  A♭/E♭  E♭
Open your eyes, look up to the skies and see.
Cm7                   F7
I'm just a poor boy, I need no sympathy.
```

cont.

B B♭ A B♭
Because I'm easy come, easy go,

B B♭ A B♭
Little high, little low.

E♭ B♭/D
Anyway the wind blows

C♯dim F7 B♭
Doesn't really matter to me, to me.

Verse 1

B♭ Gm
Mama, just killed a man,

Cm F7
Put a gun against his head, pulled my trigger, now he's dead.

B♭ Gm
Mama, life had just begun,

Cm Gaug/B Cm7/B♭ Am7♭5 A♭maj7 E♭/G
But now I've gone and thrown it all away.

E♭ B♭/D Cm
Mama, ooh,

Fm Fm/E Fm7/E♭ Dm7♭5
Didn't mean to make you cry.

B♭ B♭7 E♭
If I'm not back again this time tomor - row,

B♭/D Cm A♭m E♭
Carry on, carry on, as if nothing really mat - ters.

| A♭/E♭ E♭ Cdim7 Fm7/E♭ | B♭ | B♭ ||

Verse 2

B♭ Gm
Too late, my time has come,

Cm F7
Sent shivers down my spine, body's achin' all the time.

B♭ Gm
Goodbye everybody, I've got to go,

Cm Gaug/B Cm7/B♭ Am7♭5 A♭maj7 E♭/G
Gotta leave you all behind______ and face_____ the truth.

E♭ B♭/D Cm
Mama, ooh, (Anyway the wind blows.)

Fm Fm/E Fm7/E♭ Dm7♭5
I don't want to____ die,

B♭ B♭7
I sometimes wish I'd never been born at all.

Guitar solo

| E♭ B♭/D | Cm | Fm Fm/E Fm7/E♭ Dm7♭5 | B♭ B♭7 |

| E♭ B♭/D | Cm | Fm Fm/E Fm7/E♭ Dm7♭5 | D♭ D♭/C D♭/C♭ D♭/B♭ |

| A* ||

Interlude 1

D/A A** Adim A** D/A A** Adim
I see a little silhou - etto of a man.

A** D/A A** D/A
Scar - a - mouch, Scar - a - mouch,

A** Adim A** D/A A**
Will you do the fan - dan - go?

D♭/A♭ A♭
Thunderbolt and lightning,

C/G E7 A*
Very, very fright'ning me.

N.C.
Galileo. (Galileo.) Galileo. (Galileo.)

(Cm7)
Galileo Figaro, Magnifi - co.

B B♭ A B♭
I'm just a poor boy,

B B♭ A B♭
No - body loves me.

A♭/E♭* E♭* E♭dim E♭*
He's just a poor boy

A♭/E♭* E♭* E♭dim E♭*
From a poor fami - ly.

A♭ E♭/G F7 B♭ A♭ E♭ Cdim7 B♭7sus4
Spare him his life from this monstrosi - ty.

B B♭ A B♭
Easy come, easy go,

B B♭ A
Will you let me go?

cont.

N.C.
Bismillah!

E♭ B♭7
No, we will not let you go.

E♭ N.C.
Let him go! Bismillah!

B♭7
We will not let you go.

E♭ N.C.
Let him go! Bismillah!

B♭7
We will not let you go.

(E♭) B♭7
Let me go! Will not let you go.

(E♭) B♭7
{Let me go! Will not let you go. F♯
(Nev-er, nev - er, nev-er nev-er let me go.

B5 A5 D D♭ G♭ B♭ E♭
No, no, no, no, no, no, no!

N.C.
Oh, mama mia, mama mia.

E♭ A♭ Cm B♭
Mama mia let me go!

E♭ A♭ D7 Gm B♭7
Be - elze - bub has a devil put a - side for me,

For me, for me!

Breakdown | E♭ | E♭ | E♭ | F ‖

Bridge

B♭ E♭ B♭ D♭5
So you think you can stone me and spit in my eye?

B♭ A♭ Gm
So you think you can love me and leave me to die?

Fm B♭ Fm B♭
Oh, baby, can't do this to me, baby.

Fm B♭ Fm B♭
Just gotta get out,___ just gotta get right outta (here.)

Interlude 2 | E♭ | E♭ | E♭ | F |

Here.

| F♯ | B5 | A♭5 | B♭7 |

| B♭7 | B♭7 ‖

Outro

```
E♭     B♭/D   Cm   G7/B  Cm
Ooh, ooh,   ooh, ooh,  yeah.
G7/B  Cm    B♭  E♭  Gm  A♭  E♭
Ooh,  yeah.
Cm                   Gm        Cm            Gm
Nothing really matters, anyone can see.
Cm                             A♭m  A♭/B♭
Nothing really mat - ters,  nothing really matters
    E♭   A♭  E♭  Cdim7  B♭/D  D♭maj13  C  C7♭9  C7*  F
To me.
B♭     F        Fdim  C7sus4   F
Any - way the wind  blows.
```

Baggy Trousers

Words & Music by Michael Barson, Graham McPherson, Christopher Foreman,
Lee Thompson, Daniel Woodgate, Mark Bedford & Cathal Smyth

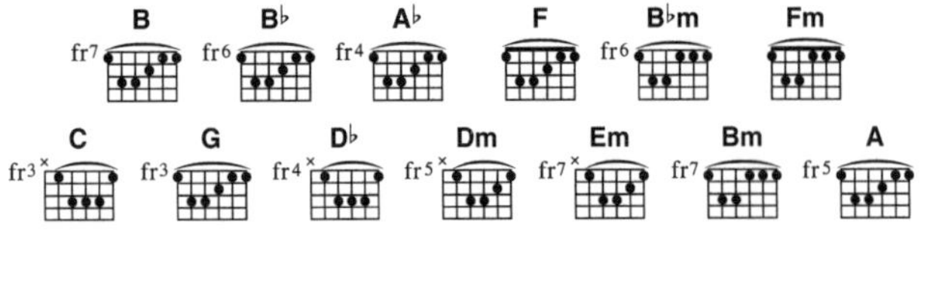

Intro | B B♭ A♭ | F | B B♭ A♭ ||

Verse 1

F A♭
Naughty boys in nasty schools, head - masters breaking all the rules.
B♭ B B♭ A♭
Having fun and playing fools, smashing up the woodwork tools.
F A♭
All the teachers in the pub, passing 'round the ready rub,
B♭ B B♭ A♭
Trying not to think of when the lunch time bell will ring a - gain.

Chorus 1

B♭ B♭m F Fm
Oh, what fun we had, but did it really turn out bad,
B♭ B♭m C G C
All I learnt at school was how to bend, not break the rules.
B♭ B♭m F Fm
Oh, what fun we had, but at the time it seemed so bad,
B♭ B♭m C B
Trying different ways to make a difference to.

Verse 2

B♭ A♭ F A♭
The head - master's had enough today, all the kids have gone away,
B♭ B B♭ A♭
Gone to fight with next door's school, every term that is the rule.
F A♭
Sits alone and bends his cane, same old backsides again,
B♭ B B♭ A♭
All the small ones tell tall tales, walking home and squashing snails.

```
              B♭               B♭m     F             Fm
*Chorus 2*    Oh, what fun we had, but did it really turn out bad,
              B♭            B♭m         C              G  C
              All I learnt at school was how to bend, not break the rules.
              B♭               B♭m     F              Fm
              Oh, what fun we had, but at the time it seemed so bad,
              B♭              B♭m    C                          D♭ (Dm)
              Trying different ways to make a difference to the days.

Instrumental 1 | Dm  Em | Dm  Bm | Dm  Em | Dm  Bm |

               | Dm  Em | Dm  Bm | Dm  Em | Dm  B  B♭ | A  A♭ ||

              F                               A♭
Verse 3       Lots of girls and lots of boys, lots of smells and lots of noise,
              B♭                             B                    B♭  A♭
              Playing football in the park, kicking push bikes after dark.
              F                           A♭
              Baggy trousers, dirty shirt, pulling hair and eating dirt,
              B♭                               B                     B♭    A♭
              Teacher comes to break it up, back of the head with a plastic cup.

Chorus 3      As Chorus 2

Instrumental 2 As Instrumental 1

                F                A♭                B♭               B  B♭  A  A♭
Outro         ||: Baggy trousers, baggy trousers, baggy trousers.
              F                A♭               B♭                B  B♭  A  A♭
              Baggy trousers, baggy trousers, baggy trousers.              :||
                                                                  Repeat to fade
```

Brass In Pocket

Words & Music by Chrissie Hynde & James Honeyman-Scott

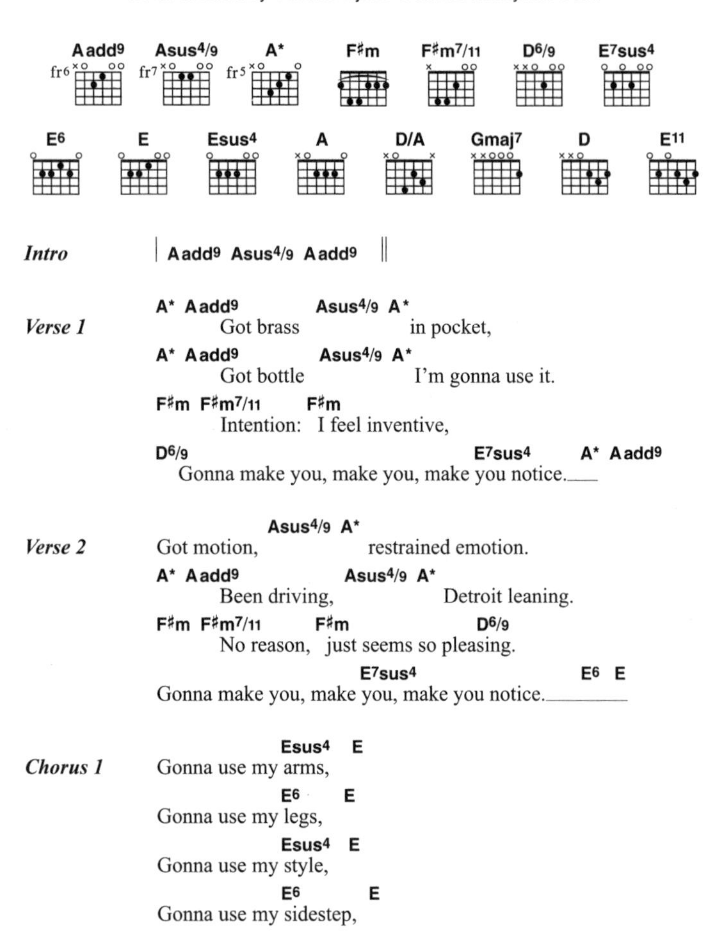

Intro | Aadd9 Asus4/9 Aadd9 ||

Verse 1

A* Aadd9 Asus4/9 A*
Got brass in pocket,
A* Aadd9 Asus4/9 A*
Got bottle I'm gonna use it.
F♯m F♯m7/11 F♯m
Intention: I feel inventive,
D6/9 E7sus4 A* Aadd9
Gonna make you, make you, make you notice.___

Verse 2

Asus4/9 A*
Got motion, restrained emotion.
A* Aadd9 Asus4/9 A*
Been driving, Detroit leaning.
F♯m F♯m7/11 F♯m D6/9
No reason, just seems so pleasing.
E7sus4 E6 E
Gonna make you, make you, make you notice._______

Chorus 1

Esus4 E
Gonna use my arms,
E6 E
Gonna use my legs,
Esus4 E
Gonna use my style,
E6 E
Gonna use my sidestep,

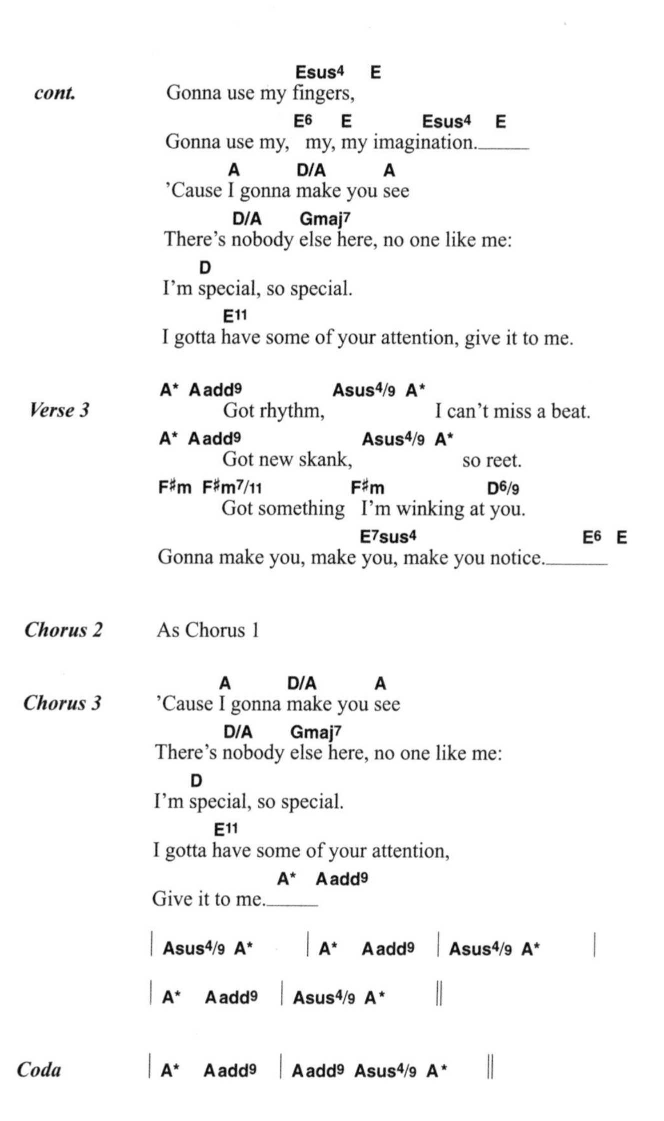

cont.

Esus4 E
Gonna use my fingers,

E6 E Esus4 E
Gonna use my, my, my imagination.___

A D/A A
'Cause I gonna make you see

D/A Gmaj7
There's nobody else here, no one like me:

D
I'm special, so special.

E11
I gotta have some of your attention, give it to me.

Verse 3

A* Aadd9 Asus4/9 A*
Got rhythm, I can't miss a beat.

A* Aadd9 Asus4/9 A*
Got new skank, so reet.

F#m F#m7/11 F#m D6/9
Got something I'm winking at you.

E7sus4 E6 E
Gonna make you, make you, make you notice.___

Chorus 2

As Chorus 1

Chorus 3

A D/A A
'Cause I gonna make you see

D/A Gmaj7
There's nobody else here, no one like me:

D
I'm special, so special.

E11
I gotta have some of your attention,

A* Aadd9
Give it to me.___

| Asus4/9 A* | A* Aadd9 | Asus4/9 A* |

| A* Aadd9 | Asus4/9 A* ||

Coda

| A* Aadd9 | Aadd9 Asus4/9 A* ||

Can't Take My Eyes Off Of You

Words & Music by Bob Crewe & Bob Gaudio

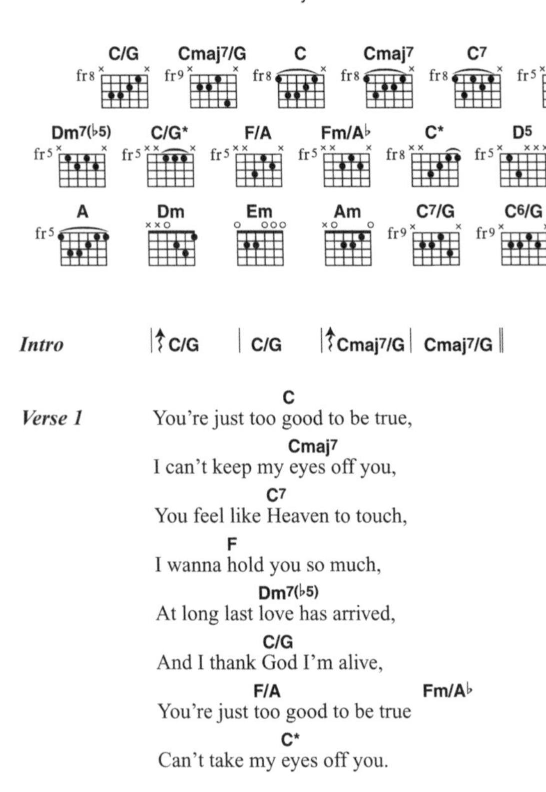

Intro | C/G | C/G | Cmaj7/G | Cmaj7/G ||

Verse 1

C
You're just too good to be true,
Cmaj7
I can't keep my eyes off you,
C7
You feel like Heaven to touch,
F
I wanna hold you so much,
Dm7(♭5)
At long last love has arrived,
C/G
And I thank God I'm alive,
F/A Fm/A♭
You're just too good to be true
C*
Can't take my eyes off you.

Verse 2

C
Pardon the way that I stare,
Cmaj7
There's nothing else to compare,
C7
The sight of you makes me weak,
F
There are no words left to speak,
Dm7(♭5)
But if you feel like I feel,
C/G
Please let me know that it's real,
F/A Fm/A♭
You're just too good to be true,
C*
Can't take my eyes off you.

Link 1

| D5 | G | C | C |
| D5 | G | C | A ||

Bridge 1

A Dm
And I love you baby,
G Em
And if it's quite all right I need you baby
Am
To warm the lonely nights,
Dm G C A
I love you baby, trust in me when I say,
Dm G
Oh, pretty baby, don't bring me down I pray,
Em Am
Oh, pretty baby, now that I've found you, stay,
Dm G
And let me love you baby, let me love you.

Verse 3 As Verse 1

Link 2 | D5 | G | C | A ||

Bridge 2 As Bridge 1

Outro | Cmaj7/G | Cmaj7/G | C7/G | C7/G |
| C6/G | C6/G | C♭6/G | C♭6/G | C/G ||

December 1963 (Oh, What A Night)

Words & Music by Judy Parker & Robert Gaudio

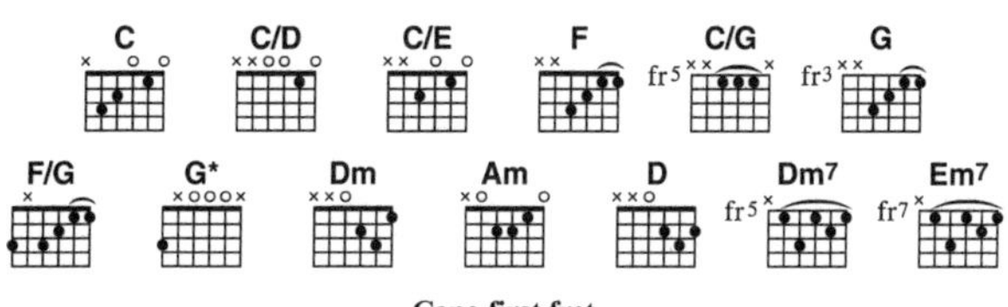

Capo first fret

Intro | C C/D C/E F | F C/G G F G | C C/D C/E F ||

Verse 1

```
F  F/G     G*      C       C/D C/E  F
        Oh, what a night,
                 C/G   G   F     G  C     C/D C/E  F
Late De - cem - ber back in 'six - ty - three,
          F/G  G*             C     C/D  C/E  F
What a ve - ry special time for   me
             C/G     G   F      G  C      C/D  C/E  F
As I re - mem - ber what a  night.
```

Verse 2

```
F  F/G     G*      C       C/D  C/E  F
        Oh, what a night,
                      C/G  G  F     G  C      C/D   C/E   F
You know I did - n't ev - en know her name,
                 F/G  G*          C  C/D  C/E    F
But I was ne - ver gonna be the  same,
            C/G   G    F      G  C       C/D  C/E  F  G
What a la  -  dy, what a  night.
```

Bridge 1

```
     Dm  F                                          Am         G
Oh, I,   I got a funny feeling when she walked in__ the room
       Dm           F                                C/G  G     C/G  G  C/G  G  F/G
That    night, as I recall it ended much too    soon.
```

Verse 3

```
C/G   G        C      C/D  C/E  F
   Oh what a night,
                C/G  G     F      G     C     C/D C/E  F
Hyp - no - ti  -  sing, mes - me - ris - ing  me,
             F/G  G*          C          C/D    C/E  F
She was ev - 'ry - thing I dreamed she'd be,
                 C/G  G    F     G  C      C/D  C/E  F  F/G  G*
Sweet sur - ren - der, what a   night.
```

Instrumental 1 | Am | Am C D | Am | Am C D ||

Bridge 2

```
Dm7                          Em7
   I felt the rush like a rolling ball of thunder,
F                                  G
Spinning my head around and taking my body under.
             (C)
Oh what a night.
```

Link |: C C/D C/E F | F C/G G F G | C C/D C/E F | F F/G G* :|

Bridge 3

```
      Dm F                              Am        G
Oh, I    got a funny feeling when she walked in__ the room
      Dm        F                            C/G  G C/G  G C/G  G F/G
That    night, as I recall it ended much too   soon.
```

Verse 4

```
C/G  G        C      C/D  C/E  F
Oh   what a night,
              C/G  G F    G C   C/D  C/E    F
Why'd it take  so long to see the   light?
                F/G     G*         C       C/D  C/E    F
Seemed so wrong, but now it seems so    right,
          C/G  G  F     G  C     C/D  C/E  F  F/G  G*
What a la  -  dy, what a   night.
```

```
Instrumental 2| Am         | Am  C  D | Am         | Am  C  D ||

                  Dm7                       Em7
Bridge 4      Oh, I felt the rush like a rolling ball of thunder,
              F                                  G
              Spinning my head around and taking my body under.

              (G)          (C)
Outro         Oh what a night.
                 C        C/D     C/E F                            C/G
              |: Doo do doo do doo do do, doo do doo do doo.
              G      F    G   C
                 Oh what a night.
                      C/D     C/E F                          F/G
              Doo do doo do doo do do, doo do doo do doo.
                  G*        C
              Oh what a night. :|   Repeat to fade
```

Come Away With Me

Words & Music by Norah Jones

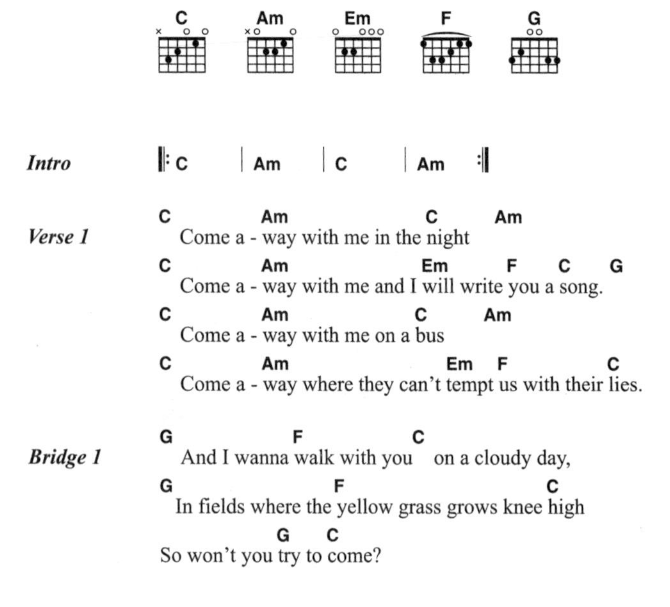

Verse 2

```
              Am                            C
Come a - way with me and we'll kiss,
       Am
On a mountain top.
C           Am                   Em
   Come a - way with me and I'll
        F          C      G
Never stop loving you.
```

Guitar solo

```
| C       | Am      | C       | Am      |
| C       | Am      | Em      | F       | C       | G       |
| C       | Am      | C       | Am      |
| C       | Am      | Em      | F       | C       | C       |
```

Bridge 2

```
G                  F
   And I wanna wake up,
              C
With the rain falling on a tent roof.
G                F                      C
   While I'm safe there in your arms,
      G           C                   Am                      C        Am
All I ask is for you to come a - way with me in the night,
C              G             C
   Come a - way with me.
```

Dance The Night Away

Words & Music by Raul Malo

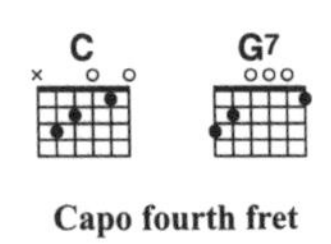

Capo fourth fret

Intro ‖: C | G7 | C | G7 :‖ *Play 3 times*

```
           C                    G7                  G7
Verse 1      Here comes my happiness a - gain
           C                 G7                   C       G7
             Right back to where it should have    been
           C                     G7               C       G7
             'Cause now she's gone and I am    free
           C                 G7               C      G7
             And she can't do a thing to    me

           C                 G7                   C    G7
Chorus 1     I just wanna dance the night a - way
           C                G7             C      G7
             With seno - ritas who can    sway
           C                    G7               C       G7
             Right now to - morrow's lookin' bright
           C                 G7               C      G7
             Just like the sunny mornin' light

               C                G7
Verse 2    And if you should see her
              C              G7           C
           Please let her know that I'm well
           G7                C     G7
             As you can tell
               C                G7
           And if she should tell you
               C                 G7
           That she wants me back
                    C
           Tell her no
           G7        C    G7
             I gotta go
```

Chorus 2 As Chorus 1

Instrumental |: C | G7 | C | G7 :| *Play 4 times*

Verse 3

```
   C               G7
And if you should see her
   C              G7         C
Please let her know that I'm well
G7               C    G7
   As you can tell
   C              G7
And if she should tell you
   C               G7
That she wants me back
          C
Tell her no
G7          C    G7
   I gotta go
```

Chorus 3 As Chorus 1

Chorus 4 As Chorus 1

Outro |: C | G7 | C | G7 :|

| C | G7 | C | C ||

Daydream Believer

featured in the Television Series THE MONKEES

Words & Music by John Stewart

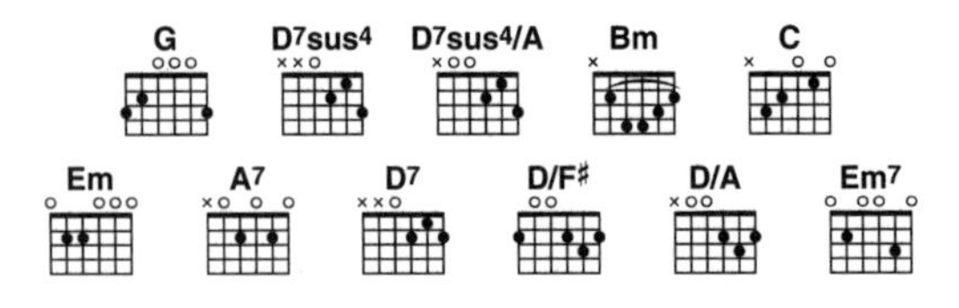

Intro | G | D7sus4 | G | D7sus4 ||

Verse 1

```
(D7sus4)      G                    D7sus4/A     Bm                  C
Oh, I could hide 'neath the wings of the bluebird as she sings,
       G                  Em                     A7     D7
The six o'clock a - larm would never ring.
         G                 D7sus4/A         Bm                  C
But it rings and I rise, wipe the sleep out of my eyes,
       G          Em        Am7        D7        G         D/F♯  G  D/A  G  D/F♯  Em7
My shaving razor's       cold and it stings.
```

Chorus 1

```
C              D          Bm    C            D        Em
Cheer up, sleepy Jean, oh what can it mean
C    G                    C                G   Em                A7          D7
To a     daydream be - liever and a     home-coming queen?
```

Verse 2

```
G                                   D7sus4/A  Bm                        C
You once thought of me as a     white knight on his steed,
G                              Em              A7    D7
Now you know how happy I can be.
                    G                                     D7sus4/A        Bm             C
Oh, and our good times start and end without dollar one to spend,
       G                 Em       Am7    D7        G           D/F♯  G  D/A  G  D/F♯  Em7
But how much baby, do we really need?
```

Chorus 2

```
C           D        Bm   C          D       Em
Cheer up, sleepy Jean, oh what can it mean
C    G                   C               G  Em            A7        D7
To a    daydream be - liever and a    home-coming queen?
C           D        Bm   C          D       Em
Cheer up, sleepy Jean, oh what can it mean
C    G                   C               G  Em            A7        D7
To a    daydream be - liever and a    home-coming queen?
```

Instrumental | G | D7sus4 | G | D7sus4 ||

Chorus 3

```
   C           D        Bm   C          D       Em
|: Cheer up, sleepy Jean, oh what can it mean
C    G                   C               G  Em            A7        D7
To a    daydream be - liever and a    home-coming queen?
C           D        Bm   C          D       Em
Cheer up, sleepy Jean, oh what can it mean
C    G                   C               G  Em            A7        D7
To a    daydream be - liever and a    home-coming queen?   :|
```

Repeat to fade

Do Right Woman, Do Right Man

Words & Music by Dan Penn & Chips Moman

F♯m E A D/A E7 D B7 A/E E7sus4/6 C♯m (fr4)

Intro | F♯m | E | A | D/A | A |

Verse 1

```
              D/A                E7
Take me to heart and I'll always love you
          D                    A
And no - body can make me do wrong.
                                    E7
Take me for granted leaving love un - shown,
                   D                  A
Makes willpower weak and temptation strong.
```

Pre-chorus 1

```
B7
   A woman's only human, you should understand,
E7
   She's not just a plaything, she's flesh and blood just like a man.
```

Chorus 1

```
                 D/A  A/E   D   A     B7
If you wanna do    right  all  days woman (woman),
                    E7sus4/6  E7     E7sus4/6  E7    A
You've gotta be a do          right  all       night man (man).
```

Bridge

```
       F♯m
Yeah, yeah, they say that it's a man's world,
C♯m
   But you can't prove that by me.
F♯m
   And as long as we're together baby,
E7
Show some respect for me.
```

Chorus 2

```
                   D/A  A/E  D   A   B7
If you wanna do    right  all  days woman (woman),
                         E7sus4/6 E7    E7sus4/6 E7   A
You've gotta be a do           right all        night man (man).
```

Pre-chorus 2

```
B7
  A woman's only human, this you should understand,
E7
  She's not just a plaything, she's flesh and blood just like a man.
```

Chorus 3

```
                   D/A  A/E  D   A   B7
If you wanna do    right  all  days woman (woman),
                         E7sus4/6 E7    E7sus4/6 E7   A
You've gotta be a do           right all        night man,
                         E7sus4/6 E7    E7sus4/6 E7   A    D/A A D/A A
You've gotta be a do           right all        night man.
```

Down Under

Words & Music by Colin Hay & Ron Strykert

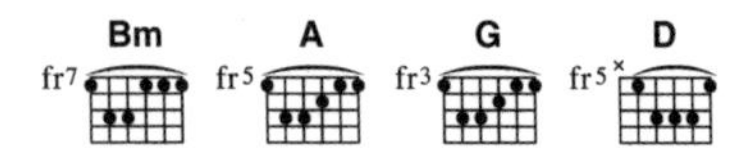

Intro | *(drums)* |: Bm A | Bm G A | Bm A | Bm G A :||

Verse 1

Bm A Bm G A
Travelling in a fried out combie
Bm A Bm G A
On a hippie trail head full of zombie.
Bm A Bm G A
I met a strange lady, she made me nervous
Bm A Bm G A
She took me in and gave me breakfast and she said

Chorus 1

D A Bm G A
Do you come from a land down under?
D A Bm G A
Where women glow and men plun - der?
D A Bm G A
Can't you hear, can't you hear the thunder?
D A Bm G A
You better run, you better take co - ver.

Link 1 | Bm A | Bm G A | Bm A | Bm G A ||

Verse 2

Bm A Bm G A
Buying bread from a man in Brussels,
Bm A Bm G A
He was six foot four and full of muscles.
Bm A Bm G A
I said do you speak-a my language?
Bm A Bm
He just smiled and gave me a Vegemite sandwich.
G A
And he said:

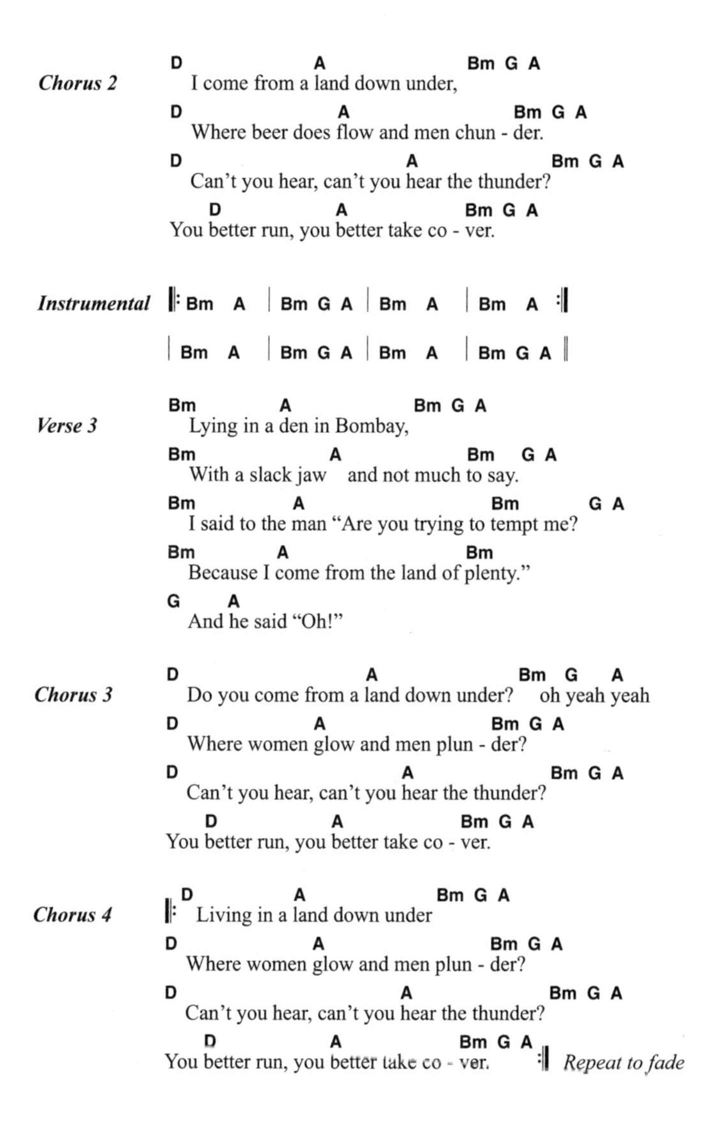
Chorus 2
D A Bm G A
I come from a land down under,
D A Bm G A
Where beer does flow and men chun - der.
D A Bm G A
Can't you hear, can't you hear the thunder?
D A Bm G A
You better run, you better take co - ver.
Instrumental
Bm A | Bm G A | Bm A | Bm A
Bm A | Bm G A | Bm A | Bm G A
Verse 3
Bm A Bm G A
Lying in a den in Bombay,
Bm A Bm G A
With a slack jaw and not much to say.
Bm A Bm G A
I said to the man "Are you trying to tempt me?
Bm A Bm
Because I come from the land of plenty."
G A
And he said "Oh!"
Chorus 3
D A Bm G A
Do you come from a land down under? oh yeah yeah
D A Bm G A
Where women glow and men plun - der?
D A Bm G A
Can't you hear, can't you hear the thunder?
D A Bm G A
You better run, you better take co - ver.
Chorus 4
D A Bm G A
Living in a land down under
D A Bm G A
Where women glow and men plun - der?
D A Bm G A
Can't you hear, can't you hear the thunder?
D A Bm G A
You better run, you better take co - ver.
Repeat to fade

Dream A Little Dream Of Me

Words by Gus Kahn
Music by Wilbur Schwandt & Fabian Andre

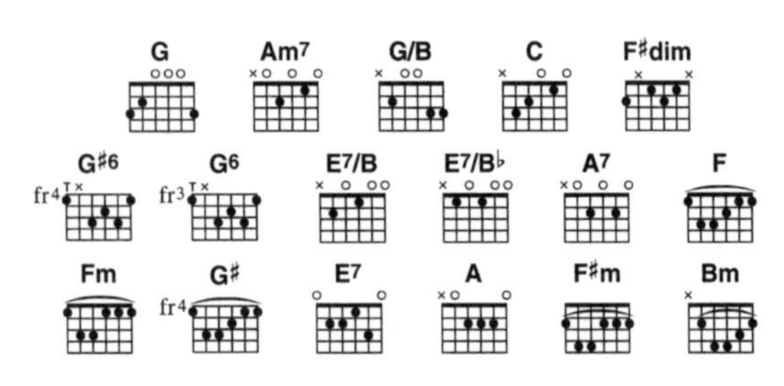

Intro G Am7 G/B ‖: C F♯dim | G♯6 G6 :‖

Verse 1

```
C        F♯dim            G♯6    G6
  Stars shining bright above you,
C          E7/B     E7/B♭     A7
  Night breezes seem to whisper, "I love you."
F                       Fm
  Birds singin' in the sycamore tree,
C              G♯          G    G6
Dream a little dream of me.
```

Verse 2

```
C      F♯dim          G♯       G
  Say nighty-night and kiss me,
C        E7/B      E7/B♭       A7
  Just hold me tight and tell me you'll miss me.
F                         Fm
  While I'm alone and blue as can be,
C              G♯        G C    E7
Dream a little dream of me.
```

Chorus 1

```
A        F♯m          Bm       E7
  Stars fading but I linger on, dear,
A       F♯m            Bm   E7
  Still craving your kiss.
A       F♯m         Bm         E7
  I'm longing to linger till dawn, dear,
A       F♯m    G♯   G
  Just saying this:__
```

Verse 3

```
C           F♯dim                  G♯6       G6
  Sweet dreams till sunbeams find you,
C          E7/B         E7/B♭     A7
  Sweet dreams that leave all worries behind you.
F                               Fm
  But in your dreams whatever they be,
C              G♯       G  C
Dream a little dream of me.
```

Piano Solo

```
| C  F♯dim | G♯   G   | C  E7/B E7/B♭ | A7     |
| F        | Fm       | C   G♯   G    | C  E7  |
```

Chorus 2

As Chorus 1

Verse 4

```
C          F♯dim                   G♯      G
  Sweet dreams till sunbeams find you,
C      E7/B           E7/B♭    A7
Sweet dreams that leave all worries far behind you.
F                                Fm
  But in your dreams whatever they be,
C              G♯      G  C
Dream a little dream of (me.)
```

Outro

```
‖: C  F♯dim | G♯   G  :‖
   me.
```

Repeat to fade with ad lib. vocal

Drops Of Jupiter (Tell Me)

Words & Music by Pat Monahan, Jimmy Stafford, Rob Hotchkiss,
Charlie Colin & Scott Underwood

Intro | C | G | F | F ||

Verse 1

C
Now that she's back in the atmosphere
G F
With drops of Jupiter in her hair, hey.__
C
She acts like summer and walks like rain,
G F
Re - minds me that there's a time to change, hey.__
C
Since the return from her stay on the moon,
G F
She listens like spring and she talks like June, hey,__ hey.

Chorus 1

G A D
But tell me, did you sail across the sun?
C/E F
Did you make it to the Milky Way

To see the lights all faded
C
And that heaven is overrated?
G A D
Tell me, did you fall for a shoot - ing star?
Dm7
One without a permanent scar

And then you missed me
F (C)
While you were looking for yourself out there.

Link 1 | C | G | F | F ||

Verse 2

```
         C
Now that she's back from that soul vacation,
G                                              F
Tracing her way through the constellation, hey.
      C
She checks out Mozart while she does Tae-Bo,
     G                                            F
Re - minds me that there's room to grow, hey.__
       C
Now that she's back in the atmosphere,
            G
I'm a - fraid that she might think of me as
F7
Plain ol' Jane told a story about a man

Who was too afraid to fly so he never did land.
```

Chorus 2

```
      G                                    A    D
But tell me, did the wind sweep you off your feet?

Did you finally get the chance
C/E   F
   To dance along the light of day
C
   And head back to the Milky Way?
      G                        A    D
And tell me, did Venus blow your mind?
                                     Dm7
Was it everything you wanted to find?

And then you missed me
                    F                          (C)
While you were looking for yourself out there.
```

Link 2 | C | G | F | F ||

Bridge

(F)   C
Can you imagine no love, pride, deep-fried chicken,
     G   F
Your best friend always sticking up for you

Even when I know you're wrong?
                                    C
Can you imagine no first dance, freeze-dried romance,
G
Five-hour phone conversation,
    B♭   F
The best soy latte that you ever had, and me?

Chorus 3

    G   A   D
But tell me, did the wind sweep you off your feet?

Did you finally get the chance
C/E   F
   To dance along the light of day
C
   And head back toward the Milky Way?
    G   A   D
But tell me, did you sail across   the sun?
                                   Dm7 F
Did you make it to the Mil - ky   Way

To see the lights all faded
C
   And that heaven is overrated?
    G   A   D
And tell me, did you fall for a shoot - ing star?
                                 Dm7
One without a permanent scar

And then you missed me
                        F
While you were looking for yourself.

Outro

C G F
(Na-na, na-na, na-na, na-na, na-na, na-na, na-na-na.)

And did you finally get the chance

To dance along the light of day?
C G F
(Na-na, na-na, na-na, na-na, na-na, na-na, na-na-na.)

And did you fall for a shooting star?

Fall for a shooting star?
C G (B♭)
(Na-na, na-na, na-na, na-na, na-na, na-na, na-na-na.)
B♭ F
And now you're lonely looking for yourself out there.

Do You Really Want To Hurt Me

Words & Music by George O'Dowd, Jonathan Moss, Roy Hay & Michael Craig

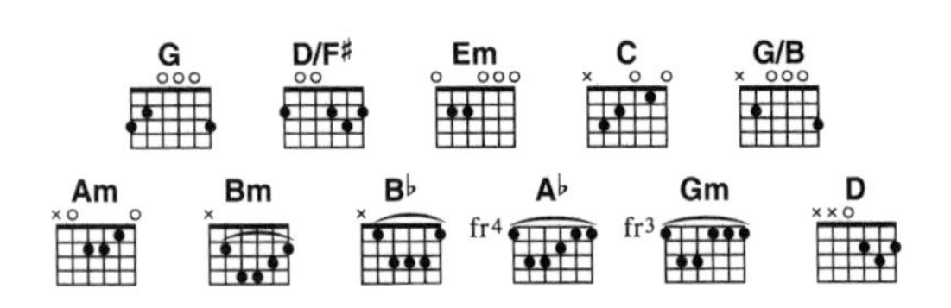

Intro

G D/F♯ Em
Give me time to realise my crime,
G D/F♯ Em
Let me love and steal.
G D/F♯ Em
I have danced inside your eyes,
G D/F♯ Em
How can I be real?

Verse 1

G D/F♯ Em
Do you really want to hurt me,
G D/F♯ Em
Do you really want to make me cry?
C G/B Am
Precious kisses, words that burn me,
Bm
Lovers never ask you why.

Verse 2

G D/F♯ Em
In my heart the fire's burning
G D/F♯ Em
Choose my colour, find a star.
C G/B Am
Precious people always tell me
Bm
That's a step, a step too far.

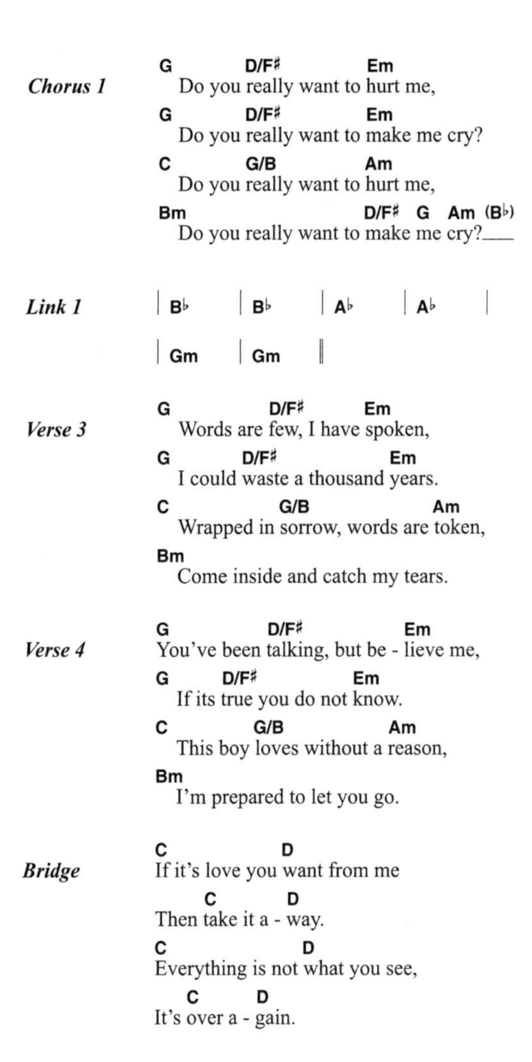

Chorus 1

G D/F♯ Em
Do you really want to hurt me,
G D/F♯ Em
Do you really want to make me cry?
C G/B Am
Do you really want to hurt me,
Bm D/F♯ G Am (B♭)
Do you really want to make me cry?___

Link 1

| B♭ | B♭ | A♭ | A♭ |
| Gm | Gm ||

Verse 3

G D/F♯ Em
Words are few, I have spoken,
G D/F♯ Em
I could waste a thousand years.
C G/B Am
Wrapped in sorrow, words are token,
Bm
Come inside and catch my tears.

Verse 4

G D/F♯ Em
You've been talking, but be - lieve me,
G D/F♯ Em
If its true you do not know.
C G/B Am
This boy loves without a reason,
Bm
I'm prepared to let you go.

Bridge

C D
If it's love you want from me
C D
Then take it a - way.
C D
Everything is not what you see,
C D
It's over a - gain.

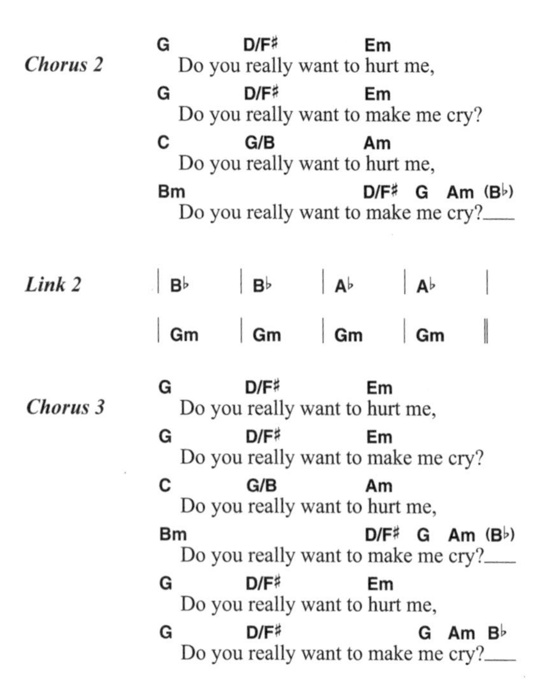

Chorus 2

G D/F♯ Em
Do you really want to hurt me,
G D/F♯ Em
Do you really want to make me cry?
C G/B Am
Do you really want to hurt me,
Bm D/F♯ G Am (B♭)
Do you really want to make me cry?___

Link 2

| B♭ | B♭ | A♭ | A♭ |
| Gm | Gm | Gm | Gm ||

Chorus 3

G D/F♯ Em
Do you really want to hurt me,
G D/F♯ Em
Do you really want to make me cry?
C G/B Am
Do you really want to hurt me,
Bm D/F♯ G Am (B♭)
Do you really want to make me cry?___
G D/F♯ Em
Do you really want to hurt me,
G D/F♯ G Am B♭
Do you really want to make me cry?___

Everybody Wants To Rule The World

Words & Music by Roland Orzabal, Ian Stanley & Chris Hughes

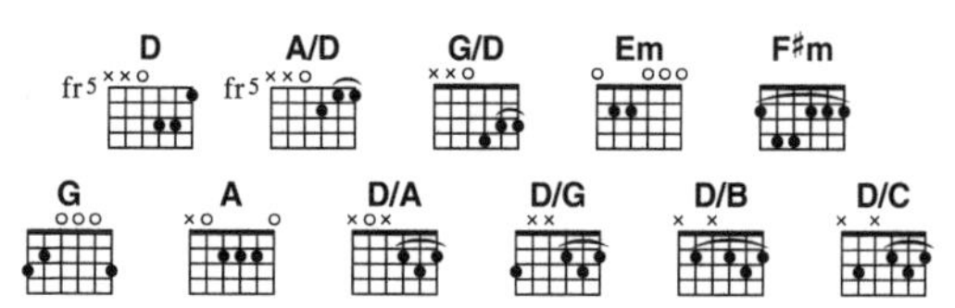

To match original recording, tune guitar slightly sharp

Intro | D | D | D | D ||

|: A/D G/D | G/D | A/D G/D | G/D :|

Verse 1

```
A/D G/D                    A/D G/D
         Welcome to your life,
                     A/D G/D
There's no turning back.
                  A/D G/D
Even while we sleep,

We will find you...
```

Chorus 1

```
Em              F#m
Acting on your best behaviour,
G                   F#m
Turn your back on Mother Nature.
Em       F#m  G       A        (A/D)
Every - body wants to rule the world.
```

Link 1 | A/D G/D | G/D | A/D G/D | G/D ||

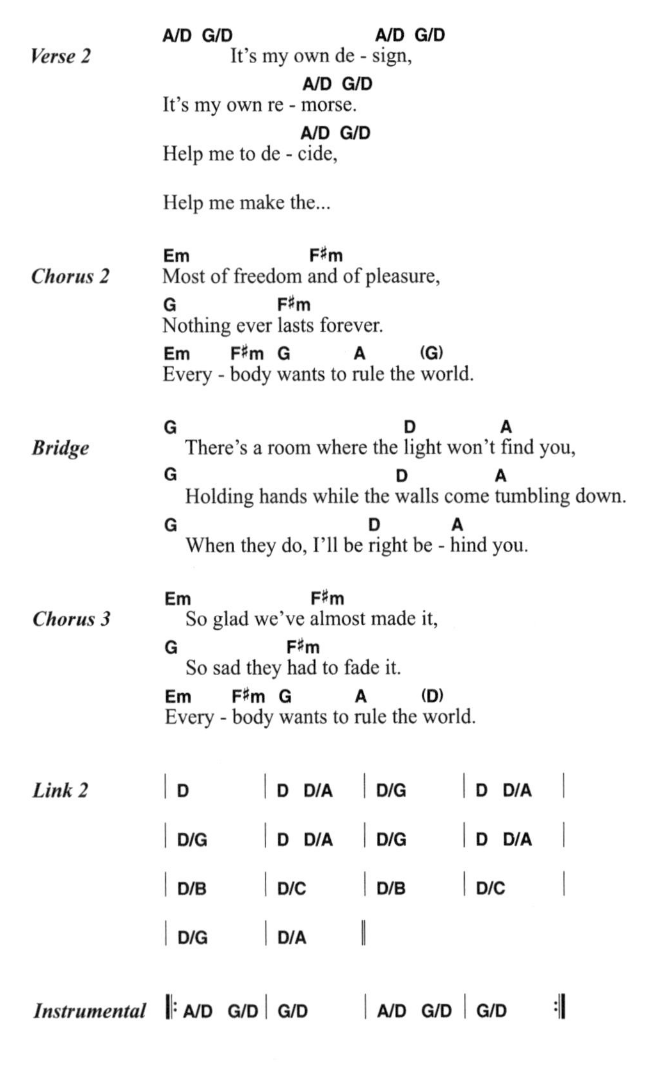
Verse 2
A/D G/D A/D G/D
It's my own de - sign,
A/D G/D
It's my own re - morse.
A/D G/D
Help me to de - cide,
Help me make the...
Chorus 2
Em F♯m
Most of freedom and of pleasure,
G F♯m
Nothing ever lasts forever.
Em F♯m G A (G)
Every - body wants to rule the world.
Bridge
G D A
There's a room where the light won't find you,
G D A
Holding hands while the walls come tumbling down.
G D A
When they do, I'll be right be - hind you.
Chorus 3
Em F♯m
So glad we've almost made it,
G F♯m
So sad they had to fade it.
Em F♯m G A (D)
Every - body wants to rule the world.
Link 2
D	D D/A	D/G	D D/A
D/G	D D/A	D/G	D D/A
D/B	D/C	D/B	D/C
D/G	D/A	
Instrumental
|: A/D G/D	G/D	A/D G/D	G/D :|

Chorus 4

```
Em                   F♯m
I can't stand this indecision
G                    F♯m
Married with a lack of vision.
Em      F♯m  G        A
Every - body wants to rule the…
Em                    F♯m
   Say that you'll never, never, never, never need it,
G                    F♯m
   One headline, why believe it?
Em      F♯m  G        A        (D)
Every - body wants to rule the world.
```

Link 3

```
| D        | D/A      | D/G      | D/A      ||
```

Chorus 5

```
Em                   F♯m
All for freedom and for pleasure,
G                 F♯m
Nothing ever lasts forever.
Em      F♯m  G        A        (A/D)
Every - body wants to rule the world.
```

Outro

```
||: A/D  G/D | G/D     | A/D  G/D | G/D     :||
```

Repeat to fade

Fire

Words & Music by Sergio Pizzorno

C5 fr8 | E♭5 fr6 | B♭5 fr6 | F5 fr8 | A♭5 fr4 | G5 fr3

Intro | C5 | C5 | C5 | C5 ||

Verse 1

C5 E♭5 B♭5 C5
Shake me into the night and I'm an easy lov - er.
E♭5 B♭5 C5
Take me into the fight and I'm an easy bro - ther.
E♭5 B♭5 C5
And I'm on fire.__

Verse 2

C5 E♭5 B♭5 C5
Burn my sweet effigy, I'm a road run - ner.
E♭5 B♭5 C5
Spill my guts on a wheel, I wanna taste, ah, huh.
E♭5 B♭5 C5 E♭5 B♭5 C5
And I'm on fire,__ and I'm on fire.__

Chorus 1

(C5) C5 F5 | E♭5 | E♭5 B♭5 | C5 |
And I'm on fire,__

C5 F5 | E♭5 | E♭5 B♭5 | C5 |
I'm on fire.__

Instrumental 1 ||: C5 F5 | E♭5 | E♭5 F5 B♭5 | C5 :||

Verse 3

C5 E♭5 B♭5 C5
Wire me up to machines, I'll be your pri - so - ner.
E♭5 B♭5 C5
Find it hard to believe, you are my mur - der - er.
E♭5 B♭5 C5 A♭5 B♭5 C5 A♭5 B♭5 G5
I'm on fire,__ look be - hind__ you, there's a fall - ing sky.

Chorus 2

(G5) C5 F5 | E♭5 | E♭5 B♭5 | C5 |
I'm on fire,____________________

C5 F5 | E♭5 | E♭5 B♭5 | C5 |
I'm on fire.____________________

Instrumental 2 ||: C5 F5 | E♭5 | E♭5 F5 B♭5 | C5 :||

Link 1

| N.C.(Cm) | N.C.(Cm) | N.C.(Cm) | N.C.(Cm) |

| C5 F5 | E♭5 | E♭5 B♭5 | C5 ||

Chorus 3

(G5) C5 F5 | E♭5 | E♭5 B♭5 | C5 |
But I'm on fire,____________________

C5 F5 | E♭5 | E♭5 B♭5 | C5 |
I'm on fire.____________________

Bridge

C5 F5 E♭5
Move on, you got to move on,
F5 B♭5 C5
You've got to give it to me, let me get the shake on.
F5 E♭5
Move on, you got to move on,
F5 B♭5 C5
You've got to give it to me, let me get the shake on.

Link 2

| C5 F5 | E♭5 | E♭5 F5 B♭5 | C5 |

| C5 F5 | E♭5 | E♭5 F5 B♭5 | C5 ||

Chorus 4

(G5) C5 F5 | E♭5 | E♭5 B♭5 | C5 |
I'm on fire,____________________

C5 F5 | E♭5 | E♭5 B♭5 | C5 |
I'm on fire.____________________

Outro | C5 F5 | E♭5 | E♭5 F5 B♭5 | C5 | C5 ||

Go Your Own Way

Words & Music by Lindsey Buckingham

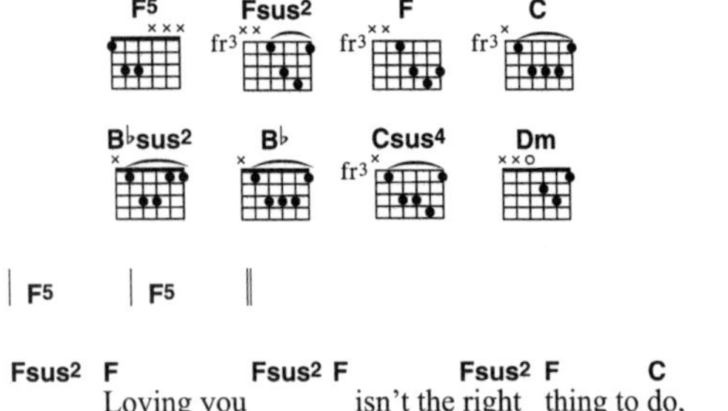

Intro | F5 | F5 ||

Verse 1

```
Fsus2  F          Fsus2 F          Fsus2 F       C
       Loving you         isn't the right  thing to do,
B♭sus2 B♭        B♭sus2 B♭             B♭sus2 B♭      Fsus2 F
       How can I        ever change things     that I feel?
Fsus2  F         Fsus2 F           Fsus2 F       C        Csus4 C
       If I could,       baby I'd give     you my world,
B♭sus2 B♭        B♭sus2 B♭                 B♭sus2 B♭      Fsus2 F
       How can I        when you won't take it    from me?
```

Chorus 1

```
Dm          B♭              C
  You can go your own way,

(Go your own way)
Dm          B♭      C
  You can call it another lonely day.
Dm          B♭              C
  You can go your own way,

Go your own way.
```

Verse 2

```
Fsus2  F             Fsus2 F
       Tell me why,
Fsus2        F       C      Csus4 C
Everything turned around.
B♭sus2 B♭             B♭sus2 B♭                  B♭sus2 B♭       Fsus2 F
       Packing up,           shacking up's all you wanna do.
Fsus2  F           Fsus2 F              Fsus2 F       C        Csus4 C
       If I could,       baby I'd give        you my world,
B♭sus2 B♭          B♭sus2 B♭                  B♭sus2 B♭   F    Fsus2 F
       Open up,           everything's waiting for you.
```

Chorus 2 As Chorus 1

Guitar solo

Fsus2 F	Fsus2 F	Fsus2 F	C
B♭sus2 B♭	B♭sus2 B♭	B♭sus2 B♭	F
Fsus2 F	Fsus2 F	Fsus2 F	C
B♭sus2 B♭	B♭sus2 B♭	B♭sus2 B♭	F	

Chorus 3

```
Dm          B♭              C
   You can go your own way,

(Go your own way)
Dm          B♭              C
   You can call it anoth - er lonely day.

(Another lonely day)
Dm          B♭              C
   You can go your own way,

(Go your own way)
Dm          B♭              C
   You can call it anoth - er lonely day.
```

Outro |: Dm | B♭ | C | C :| *Repeat to fade*

A Groovy Kind Of Love

Words & Music by Toni Wine & Carole Bayer Sager

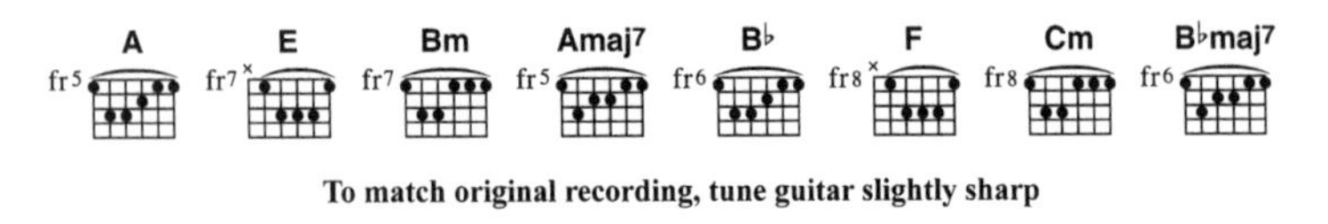

To match original recording, tune guitar slightly sharp

Intro | A | E | A ||

Verse 1

```
A                                    E
When I'm feeling blue, all I've got to do
                    A               Bm
Is take a look at you, then I'm not so blue.
E                       Bm  E              Amaj7
When you're close to me,  I can feel your heartbeat,
                 Bm                 E
I can feel you      breathing in my ear.
                   A               E                    A
Wouldn't you a - gree, baby you and me got a groovy kind of love?
E                     A                E
   Got a groovy kind of love. (Groovy kind of love.)
```

Verse 2

```
A                                        E
Anytime you want to you can turn me on to
                   A                 Bm
Anything you want to, anytime at all.
E                     Bm  E               Amaj7
When you kiss my lips, oh, I start to shiver,
                        Bm             E
Can't control the quivering in - side.
                   A               E                    A
Wouldn't you a - gree, baby you and me got a groovy kind of love?
E                     A
   Got a groovy kind of love.
```

Instrumental | B♭ | F | B♭ | Cm F ||

```
            (F)                     Cm    F                    B♭maj7
*Verse 3*   When I'm in your arms, nothing seems to matter,
                                     Cm                F
            If the world should shatter, I don't care.
                                 B♭                     F                        B♭
            Wouldn't you a - gree, baby you and me got a groovy kind of love?
            F                         B♭
              Got a groovy kind of love.
            F                            B♭
              We got a groovy kind of love.
```

Have I Told You Lately

Words & Music by Van Morrison

F♯m11 B11 Eadd9 G♯m7 Amaj7

fr4

Intro | F♯m11 | B11 |

| Eadd9 G♯m7 | Amaj7 B11 | Eadd9 G♯m7 | Amaj7 B11 |

| Amaj7 | G♯m7 | F♯m11 B11 | Eadd9 B11 ||
(Have I)

Chorus 1

(B11) Eadd9 G♯m7 Amaj7 B11
Have I told you lately that I love you?
Eadd9 G♯m7 Amaj7 B11 Amaj7
Have I told you there's no one a - bove you?
G♯m7
Fill my heart with gladness,
F♯m11
Take away my sadness and
B11 Eadd9 B11
Ease my troubles, that's what you do.

Verse 1

Eadd9 G♯m7 Amaj7 B11
Oh the morn - ing sun in all its glory,
Eadd9 G♯m7 Amaj7 B11 Amaj7
Greets the day with hope and comfort too.
G♯m7
And you fill my life with laughter,
F♯m11
You can make it better,
B11 Eadd9 F♯m11 G♯m7
Ease my troubles that's what you do.

Bridge 1

```
Amaj7
   There's a love that's divine,
                                             G#m7
And it's yours and it's mine like the sun.
Amaj7
   At the end of the day,
                                                G#m7   B11
We should give thanks and pray to the One.
```

Chorus 2

```
     Eadd9                G#m7             Amaj7      B11
Say,        have I told you       lately that I love  you?
Eadd9          G#m7                    Amaj7      B11  Amaj7
   Have I told you there's no one a - bove you?
                                   G#m7
Fill my heart with gladness,
                              F#m11
Take away my sadness,
           B11                          Eadd9   B11
Ease my troubles, that's what you do.
```

Piano Solo

Eadd9 G#m7	Amaj7 B11
Eadd9 G#m7	Amaj7 B11
Amaj7	G#m7
F#m11 B11	Eadd9 F#m11 G#m7 ‖

Bridge 2

```
Amaj7
   There's a love that's divine,

And it's yours and it's mine,
     G#m7
And it shines like the sun.
     Amaj7
At the end of the day,
                                             G#m7    B11
We will give thanks and pray to the One.
```

Chorus 3

```
(B11)      Eadd9    G#m7          Amaj7         B11
   Have I told you lately that I love you?
Eadd9      G#m7                      Amaj7                 B11   Amaj7
   Have I told you there's no one          above you?
                                    G#m7
Fill my heart with gladness,
                                    F#m11
Take away my sadness and
           B11                            Eadd9    F#m11   G#m7
Ease my troubles, that's what you do.
```

Outro

```
Amaj7                             G#m7
   Take away my sadness,
                                       F#m11
Fill my life with gladness yeah,
           B11                            Eadd9    F#m11   G#m7   Amaj7
Ease my troubles that's what you do.
                                  G#m7
Fill my life with gladness,
                              F#m11
Take away my sadness,
           B11                            Eadd9
Ease my troubles that's what you do.
```

Holding Back The Years

Words by Mick Hucknall
Music by Mick Hucknall & Neil Moss

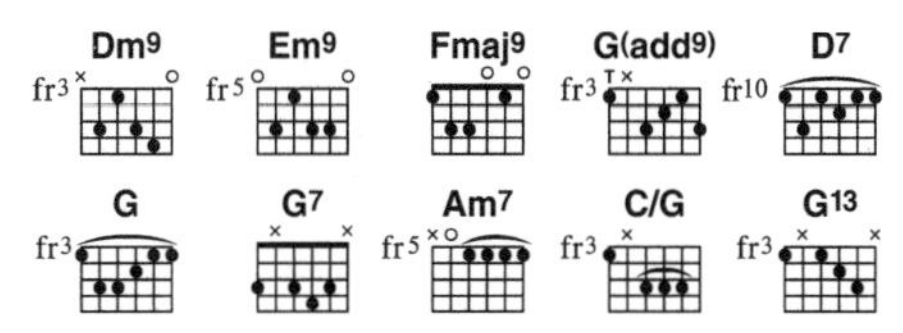

To match original recording, tune guitar slightly sharp

Intro

| Dm9 | Em9 | Fmaj9 | Gadd9 |

| D7 | Em9 | Fmaj9 | G |

Verse 1

Dm9 G7 Am7 Dm9
Holding back the years,
G7 Am7 Dm9
Thinking of the fear I've had for so long.
G7 Am7 Dm9
When somebo - dy hears,___
G7 C/G G7
Listen to the fear that's gone.

Verse 2

Dm9 G7 Am7 Dm9
Strangled by the wishes of pa - ter,
G7 Am7 Dm9
Hoping for the arms of ma - ter,
G7 C/G G7
Get to me the sooner or later, oh.

Link 1

| Dm9 | G13 | Dm9 | G13 |

Verse 3

Dm9 G7 Am7 Dm9
Holding back the years,

G7 Am7 Dm9
Chance for me to escape from all I know.

G7 Am7 Dm9
Holding back the tears,___

G7 C/G G7
'Cause nothing here has grown.___

Verse 4

Dm9 G7 Am7 Dm9
I've wasted all my tears,

G7 Am7 Dm9
Wasted all those years.

G7 Am7 Dm9
Nothing had the chance to be good,

G7 C/G G7
Nothing ever could, yeah,___ oh well.

Chorus 1

Dm9 G13
I'll keep___ holding on,

Dm9 G13
I'll keep___ holding on,

Dm9 G13
I'll keep___ holding on,

Dm9 G7 C/G G7 (Dm9)
I'll keep___ holding on so tight.

Trumpet solo | Dm9 | G7 Am7 | Dm9 | G7 |

C/G G7 C/G G7 C/G G7
All right, oh, now,

Verse 5

G7 Dm9 G7 Am7 Dm9
Well, I've___ wasted all my tears,

G7 Am7 Dm9
Wasted all___ of those years.

G7 Am7 Dm9
And nothing had the chance to be good,

G7
'Cause nothing ever could.

C/G G7
Oh yeah, oh.

Chorus 2

```
Dm9         G13
   I'll keep___ holding on,
Dm9         G13
   I'll keep___ holding on,
Dm9         G13
   I'll keep___ holding on,
Dm9         G7                C/G  G7
   I'll keep___ holding on,
                    C/G  G7
Holding, holding,             holding,
    Dm9           G13
Oh,___ la ma la la la la.
     Dm9     G13
I say,    ooh well,
Dm9               G7
   It's all I have today,
Dm9               G7
   It's all I have to say.
```

Outro

```
‖: Dm9  | G7  | Dm9  | G7  :‖
```
Repeat to fade

Help Me Make It Through The Night

Words & Music by Kris Kristofferson

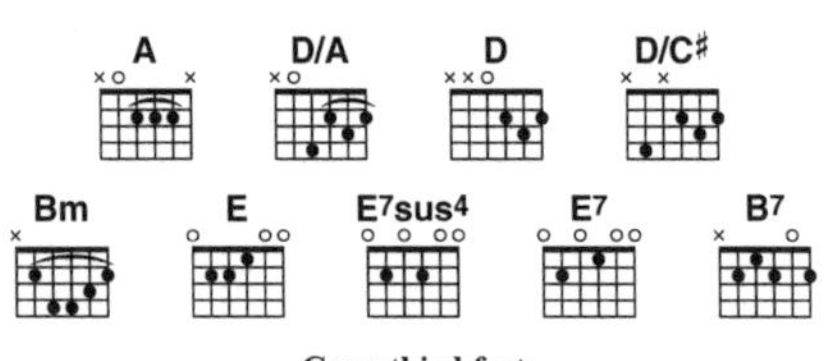

Capo third fret

Intro | A | D/A | A ||

Verse 1

N.C. A D/A A
Take the ribbon from your hair,
D D/C♯ Bm
Shake it loose and let it fall.
E E7sus4 E7 E7sus4
Laying soft upon my skin,
E A
Like the shadows on the wall.

Verse 2

N.C. A D/A A
Come and lay down by my side,
D D/C♯ Bm
Till the early morning light.
E E7sus4 E7 E7sus4
All I'm taking is your time,
E A D/A A
Help me make it through the night.

Bridge

A D
I don't care who's right or wrong,
A
I don't try to unders - tand.
B7
Let the devil take to - morrow,
E E7sus4 E7 E7sus4
Lord, tonight I need a friend.

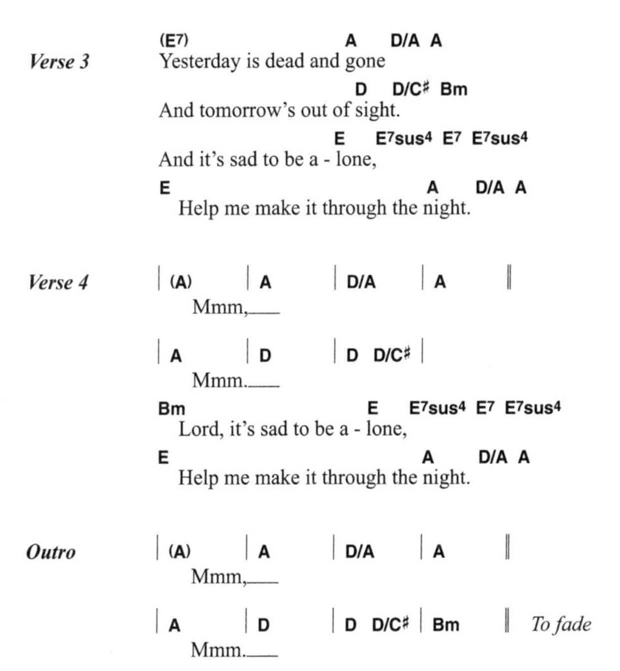
Verse 3
(E7) A D/A A
Yesterday is dead and gone
D D/C♯ Bm
And tomorrow's out of sight.
E E7sus4 E7 E7sus4
And it's sad to be a - lone,
E A D/A A
Help me make it through the night.
Verse 4
(A) | A | D/A | A
Mmm,
A | D | D D/C♯
Mmm.
Bm E E7sus4 E7 E7sus4
Lord, it's sad to be a - lone,
E A D/A A
Help me make it through the night.
Outro
(A) | A | D/A | A
Mmm,
A | D | D D/C♯ | Bm
To fade
Mmm.

The House Of The Rising Sun

Words & Music by Alan Price

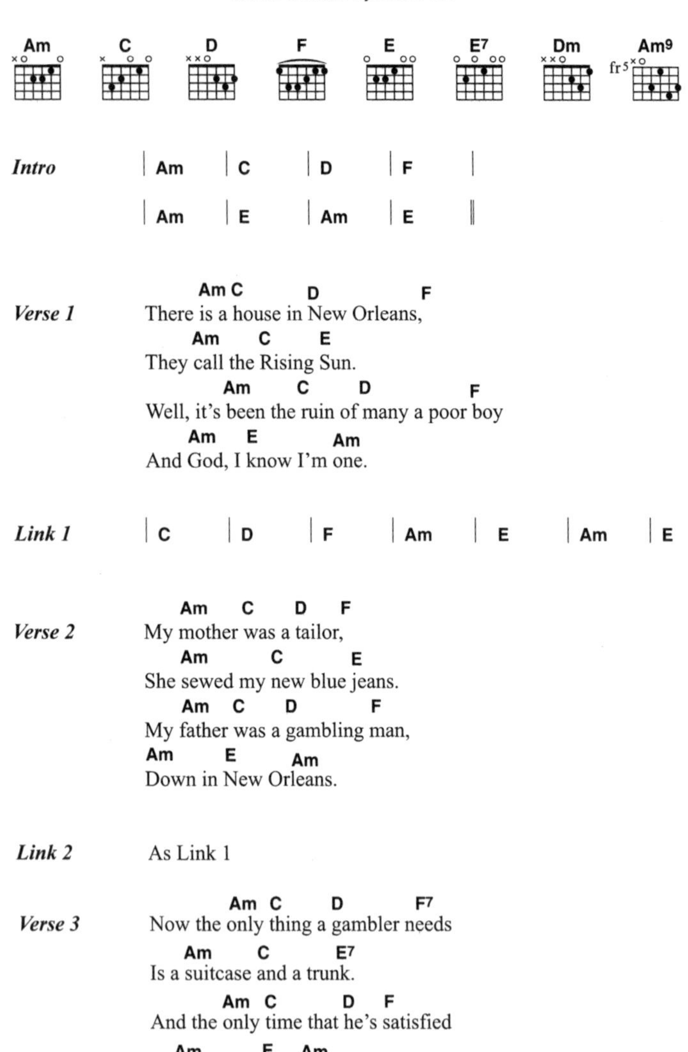

Intro

| Am | C | D | F |

| Am | E | Am | E ||

Verse 1

Am C D F
There is a house in New Orleans,
Am C E
They call the Rising Sun.
Am C D F
Well, it's been the ruin of many a poor boy
Am E Am
And God, I know I'm one.

Link 1

| C | D | F | Am | E | Am | E

Verse 2

Am C D F
My mother was a tailor,
Am C E
She sewed my new blue jeans.
Am C D F
My father was a gambling man,
Am E Am
Down in New Orleans.

Link 2

As Link 1

Verse 3

Am C D F7
Now the only thing a gambler needs
Am C E7
Is a suitcase and a trunk.
Am C D F
And the only time that he's satisfied
Am E Am
Is when he's on a drunk.

Link 3 As Link 1

Solo

```
| Am    | C     | D     | F     |
| Am    | C     | E7    | E7    |
| Am    | C     | D     | F     |
| Am    | E     | Am    | C     |
| D     | F     | Am    | E7    | Am    | E7    |
```

Verse 4

```
     Am      C            D        F
Oh mother,   tell your children,
          Am       C       E
Not to do what I have done.
Am              C        D         F
Spend your lives in sin and misery,
        Am                E        Am
In the House of the Rising Sun.
```

Link 4 As Link 1

Verse 5

```
       Am       C       D         F
I got one foot on the platform,
     Am          C       E
The other foot on the train.
    Am    C          D             F
I'm going back to New Orleans,
   Am           E           Am
To wear that ball and chain.
```

Link 5 As Link 1

Verse 6 As Verse 1

Outro

```
| C     | D     | F     | Am    |
| E     | Am    | Dm    | Am    |
| Dm    | Am    | Dm    | Am    |
| Dm    | Am    | Dm    | Am9   ||
```

How To Save A Life

Words & Music by Joseph King & Isaac Slade

G D/F# C D(add11) Em7 Em7*

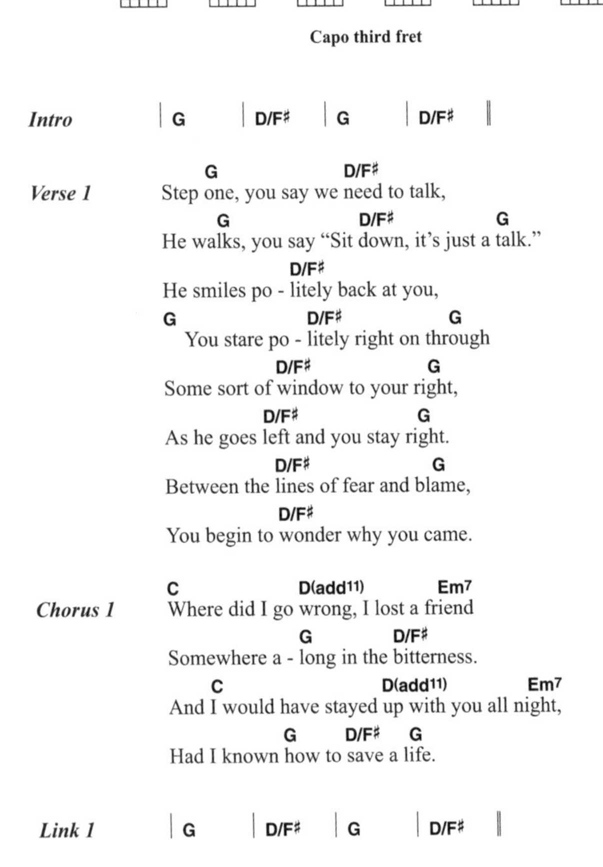

Capo third fret

Intro | G | D/F# | G | D/F# ‖

Verse 1

```
     G                     D/F#
Step one, you say we need to talk,
      G                     D/F#          G
He walks, you say "Sit down, it's just a talk."
                D/F#
He smiles po - litely back at you,
G                  D/F#              G
   You stare po - litely right on through
                 D/F#              G
Some sort of window to your right,
                D/F#              G
As he goes left and you stay right.
                 D/F#              G
Between the lines of fear and blame,
                 D/F#
You begin to wonder why you came.
```

Chorus 1

```
C                  D(add11)          Em7
Where did I go wrong, I lost a friend
                   G             D/F#
Somewhere a - long in the bitterness.
      C                     D(add11)             Em7
And I would have stayed up with you all night,
                 G       D/F#    G
Had I known how to save a life.
```

Link 1 | G | D/F# | G | D/F# ‖

Verse 2

G D/F♯
Let him know that you know best,
Em7* D/F♯
'Cause after all you do know best.
G D/F♯
Try to slip past his defence
Em7* D/F♯
Without granting innocence.
G D/F♯ Em7*
Lay down a list of what is wrong,
D/F♯
The things you've told him all along.
G D/F♯
Pray to God he hears you
Em7* D/F♯
And pray to God he hears you.

Chorus 2

C D(add11) Em7
And where did I go wrong, I lost a friend
G D/F♯
Somewhere a - long in the bitterness.
C D(add11) Em7
And I would have stayed up with you all night,
G D/F♯ G
Had I known how to save a life.

Link 2

| G | D/F♯ | Em7* | D/F♯ ‖

Verse 3

G D/F♯
As he begins to raise his voice,
Em7* D/F♯ G
You lower yours and grant him one last choice.
D/F♯
Drive until you lose the road
Em7* D/F♯
Or break with the ones you've followed.
G D/F♯
He will do one of two things,
Em7* D/F♯
He will admit to everything
G D/F♯
Or he'll say he's just not the same
Em7* D/F♯
And you'll begin to wonder why you came.

Chorus 3 As Chorus 1

Chorus 4 As Chorus 1

```
         G  D/F♯  G  D/F♯                G   D/F♯  G
Link 3                   How to save a life.
         D/F♯              G   D/F♯
         How to save a life.
```

Chorus 5 As Chorus 1

Chorus 6 As Chorus 1

```
         G  D/F♯  G  D/F♯                G   D/F♯  G
Outro                    How to save a life.
         D/F♯              G   D/F♯  G  D/F♯  G
         How to save a life.
```

I Bet You Look Good On The Dance Floor

Words & Music by Alex Turner

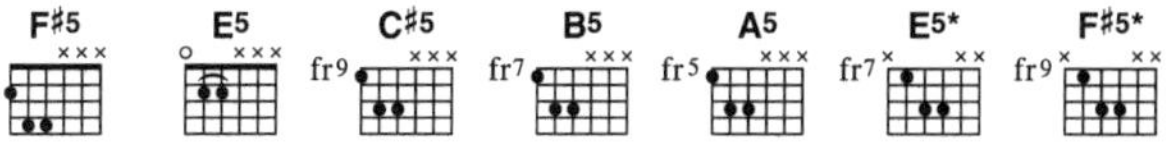

F♯5 | E5 | C♯5 (fr9) | B5 (fr7) | A5 (fr5) | E5* (fr7) | F♯5* (fr9)

Intro

𝄆 F♯5 E5 | F♯5 E5 | F♯5 E5 | F♯5 E5 𝄇

𝄆 F♯5 | F♯5 | F♯5 | F♯5 𝄇

𝄆 C♯5 B5 | A5 F♯5 | C♯5 B5 | A5 F♯5 𝄇

Verse 1

C♯5 B5 A5 F♯5 C♯5 B5 A5 F♯5
Stop making the eyes at me, I'll stop making the eyes at you
C♯5 B5 A5 F♯5 C♯5 B5 A5
And what it is that sur - prises me is that I don't really want you to.

Pre-chorus 1

(A5) F♯5 C♯5 B5 A5
And your shoulders are frozen, (cold as the night).
F♯5 C♯5 B5 A5
Oh, but you're an ex - plosion, (you're dyna - mite).
F♯5 C♯5 B5 A5
Your name isn't Rio but I don't care for sand,
F♯5 C♯5 B5 A5 E5
And lighting the fuse might re - sult in a bang b - b - bang, go.

Chorus 1

F♯5 A5
I bet that you look good on the dancefloor,
E5*
I don't know if you're looking for ro - mance or,
F♯5*
I don't know what you're looking for.
F♯5 A5
I said I bet that you look good on the dancefloor,
E5* C♯5
Dancing to electro - pop like a robot from nineteen - eighty - four,

Well, from nineteen - eighty - four.

Link 1 ‖: C♯5 B5 | A5 F♯5 | C♯5 B5 | A5 F♯5 :‖

Verse 2

C♯5 B5 A5 F♯5
I wish you'd stop ignoring me
C♯5 B5 A5 F♯5
Because you're sending me to des - pair.
C♯5 B5 A5 F♯5
Without a sound yeah, you're calling me
C♯5 B5 A5
And I don't think it's very fair...

Pre-chorus 2

(A5) F♯5 C♯5 B5 A5
That your shoulders are frozen, (cold as the night).
F♯5 C♯5 B5 A5
Oh, but you're an ex - plosion, (you're dyna - mite).
F♯5 C♯5 B5 A5
Your name isn't Rio but I don't care for sand,
F♯5 C♯5 B5 A5 E5
And lighting the fuse might re - sult in a bang b - b - bang, go.

Chorus 2

F♯5 A5
I bet that you look good on the dancefloor,
E5*
I don't know if you're looking for ro - mance or,
F♯5*
I don't know what you're looking for.
F♯5 A5
I said I bet that you look good on the dancefloor,
E5* C♯5
Dancing to electro - pop like a robot from nineteen - eighty - four,
A5
Well, from nineteen - eighty - four.

Bridge

A5 E5* F♯5*
And oh, there ain't no love, no Montagues or Capu - lets.

Just banging tunes in DJ sets and
A5 E5* (F♯5)
Dirty dance - floors and dreams of naughti - ness.

Link 2

```
||: F#5   E5 | F#5   E5 | F#5   E5 | F#5   E5 :||
| F#5       | F#5       | F#5       | F#5       |
| F#5       | F#5       | F#5       | E5*       ||
```

Chorus 3

```
F#5*      N.C.                              A5
   I wan - na bet that you look good on the dancefloor,
                                      E5*
I don't know if you're looking for ro - mance or,
                                 F#5*
I don't know what you're looking for.
F#5*                                    A5
   I said I bet that you look good on the dancefloor,
                    E5*                                          C#5
Dancing to electro - pop like a robot from nineteen - eighty - four,
                               F#5
Said from nineteen - eighty - four.
```

I Don't Wanna Dance

Words & Music by Eddy Grant

Chorus 1

B
I don't wanna dance,
F♯
Dance with you baby, no more.
Gdim7 G♯m
I'll never do something to hurt you though.
B F♯
Oh, but the feeling is bad, the feeling is bad.

Verse 1

B
I love your personality,
F♯ Gdim7
Oh, but I don't want our love on show.
G♯m
Sometimes I think it's insanity
F♯
Girl, the way you go
B
With all of the guys on the corner,
F♯ Gdim7
Oh, baby you're the latest trick.
G♯m
Oh, you seem to have their number,
F♯
Look they are dancing still.

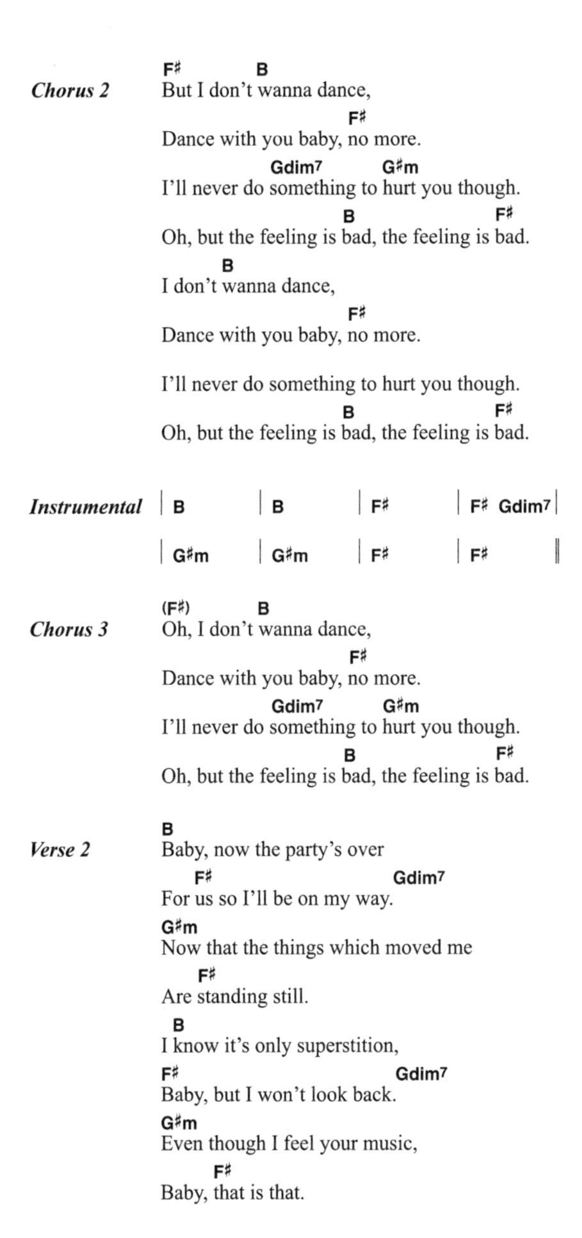

Chorus 2

F♯ B
But I don't wanna dance,
F♯
Dance with you baby, no more.
Gdim7 G♯m
I'll never do something to hurt you though.
B F♯
Oh, but the feeling is bad, the feeling is bad.
B
I don't wanna dance,
F♯
Dance with you baby, no more.

I'll never do something to hurt you though.
B F♯
Oh, but the feeling is bad, the feeling is bad.

Instrumental

| B | B | F♯ | F♯ Gdim7 |
| G♯m | G♯m | F♯ | F♯ ‖

Chorus 3

(F♯) B
Oh, I don't wanna dance,
F♯
Dance with you baby, no more.
Gdim7 G♯m
I'll never do something to hurt you though.
B F♯
Oh, but the feeling is bad, the feeling is bad.

Verse 2

B
Baby, now the party's over
F♯ Gdim7
For us so I'll be on my way.
G♯m
Now that the things which moved me
F♯
Are standing still.
B
I know it's only superstition,
F♯ Gdim7
Baby, but I won't look back.
G♯m
Even though I feel your music,
F♯
Baby, that is that.

```
             F♯          B
Chorus 4     Oh, I don't wanna dance,
                                    F♯
             Dance with you baby, no more.
                             Gdim7      G♯m
             I'll never do something to hurt you though.
                                    B              F♯
             Oh, but the feeling is bad, the feeling is bad.
                   B
             I don't wanna dance,
                                    F♯
             Dance with you baby, no more.

             I'll never do something to hurt you though.
                                    B              F♯
             Oh, but the feeling is bad, the feeling is bad.

             B
Chorus 5       I don't wanna dance, don't wanna dance.
             F♯                                   Gdim7  G♯m
               I don't wanna dance, don't wanna dance.____

             Don't wanna dance, don't wanna dance.
             B                      F♯
               Don't wanna dance.___
                         B
             Oh, I don't wanna dance,
                                    F♯
             Dance with you baby, no more.    To fade
```

I Heard It Through The Grapevine

Words & Music by Norman J. Whitfield & Barrett Strong

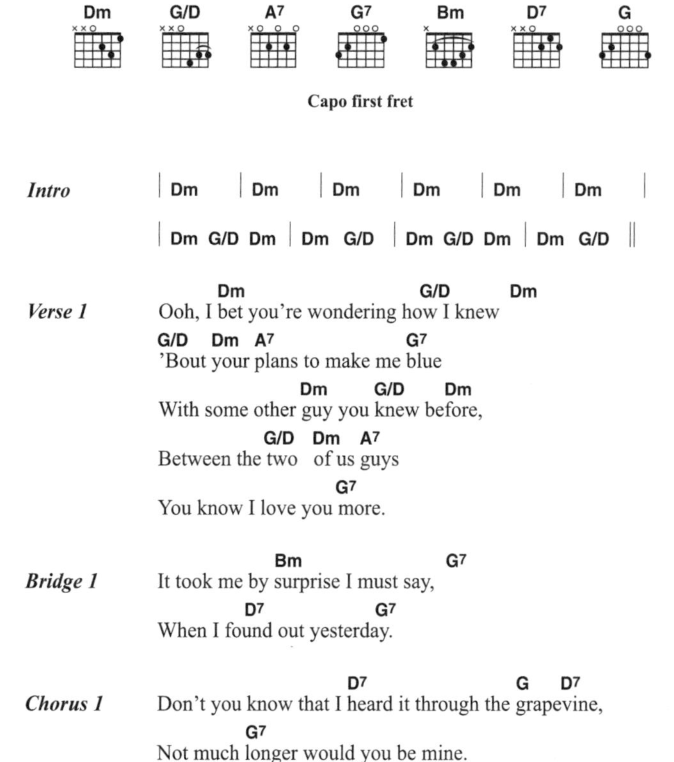

Capo first fret

Intro
| Dm | Dm | Dm | Dm | Dm | Dm |
| Dm G/D Dm | Dm G/D | Dm G/D Dm | Dm G/D ||

Verse 1
Dm G/D Dm
Ooh, I bet you're wondering how I knew
G/D Dm A7 G7
'Bout your plans to make me blue
Dm G/D Dm
With some other guy you knew before,
G/D Dm A7
Between the two of us guys
G7
You know I love you more.

Bridge 1
Bm G7
It took me by surprise I must say,
D7 G7
When I found out yesterday.

Chorus 1
D7 G D7
Don't you know that I heard it through the grapevine,
G7
Not much longer would you be mine.

cont.

```
     D7                      G    D7
Oh, I heard it through the grapevine,
                G7
Oh, and I'm just about to lose my mind.
                    | Dm     |
Honey, honey, yeah.

| Dm     | Dm     | Dm     ||
```

Verse 2

```
           Dm              G/D        Dm
I know a man ain't supposed to cry
G/D  Dm   A7                      G7
But  these tears I can't hold inside.
         Dm                    G/D      Dm
Losin' you would end my life you see,
G/D      Dm   A7                 G7
'Cause you   mean that much to me.
```

Bridge 2

```
                        Bm             G7
You could have told me yourself
             D7         G7
That you love someone else.
```

Chorus 2

```
              D7                    G    D7
Instead I heard it through the grapevine,
                G7
Not much longer would you be mine.
     D7                      G    D7
Oh, I heard it through the grapevine
          G7
And I'm just about to lose my mind.
                    | Dm     |
Honey, honey, yeah.

| Dm     | Dm     | Dm     ||
```

Link

```
| Dm G/D Dm | Dm  G/D  | Dm G/D Dm | Dm  G/D  ||
```

Verse 3

```
                           Dm    G/D       Dm
People say believe half of what you see,
G/D   Dm   A7                   G7
Son,  and  none of what you hear.
                   Dm  G/D       Dm
But I can't help   bein' confused
G/D  Dm   A7                    G7
If    it's   true please tell me dear.
```

```
             Bm              G7
Bridge 3     Do you plan to let me go
                  D7                  G7
             For the other guy you loved before?

                                D7                          G     D7
Chorus 3     Don't you know I heard it through the grapevine,
                           G7
             Not much longer would you be mine.
                    D7                        G     D7
             Baby, I heard it through the grapevine,
                             G7
             Ooh, and I'm just about to lose my mind.
                                   | Dm      |
             Honey, honey, yeah.

             | Dm    | Dm    | Dm    ||

                                   Dm
Outro        ||: Honey, honey I know

             That you're letting me go. :||   Repeat to fade
                                              with vocal ad lib.
```

I Saw The Light

Words & Music by Todd Rundgren

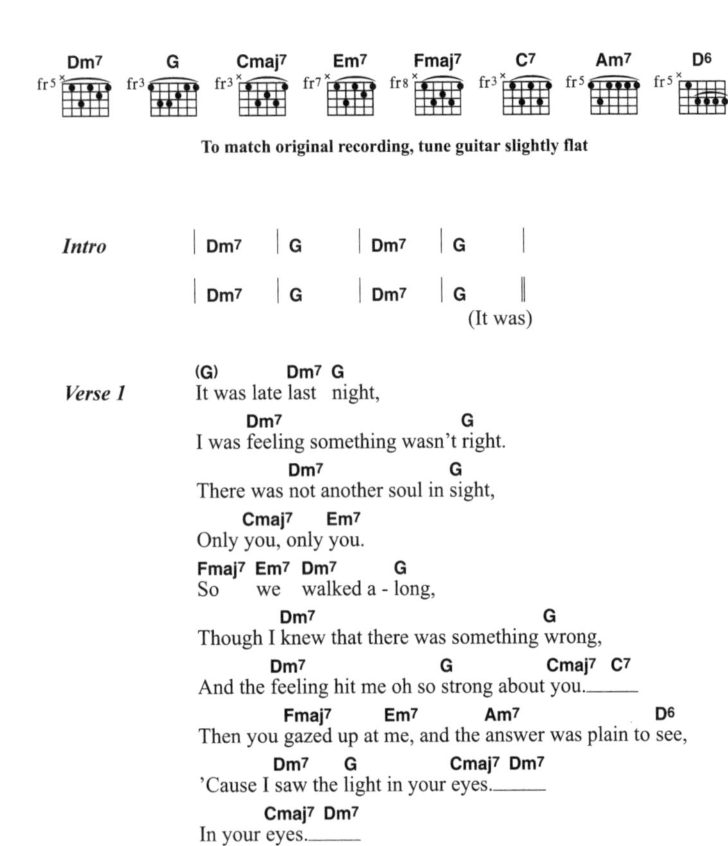

To match original recording, tune guitar slightly flat

Intro

| Dm7 | G | Dm7 | G |

| Dm7 | G | Dm7 | G ‖
(It was)

Verse 1

```
(G)              Dm7  G
It was late last  night,
         Dm7                    G
I was feeling something wasn't right.
             Dm7                G
There was not another soul in sight,
        Cmaj7    Em7
Only you, only you.
Fmaj7 Em7 Dm7        G
So     we  walked a - long,
              Dm7                       G
Though I knew that there was something wrong,
            Dm7                G              Cmaj7  C7
And the feeling hit me oh so strong about you.______
              Fmaj7        Em7          Am7                D6
Then you gazed up at me, and the answer was plain to see,
             Dm7      G              Cmaj7  Dm7
'Cause I saw the light in your eyes.______
           Cmaj7  Dm7
In your eyes.______
```

Verse 2

(Dm7) G
Though we had our fling,

Dm7 G
I just never would suspect a thing,

Dm7 G Cmaj7 Em7
Till that little bell began to ring in my head, in my head.

Fmaj7 Em7 Dm7 G
But I tried to run,

Dm7 G
Though I knew it wouldn't help me none,

Dm7 G Cmaj7 C7
'Cause I couldn't ever love no one, or so I said.___

Fmaj7 Em7 Am7 D6
But my feelings for you were just something I never knew,

Dm7 G Cmaj7 Dm7
Till I saw the light in your eyes.___

Cmaj7 Dm7 G
In your eyes.___

Solo

| Dm7 | G | Dm7 | G |

| Dm7 | G | Cmaj7 | Emaj7 Fmaj7 Em7 ‖
(But I)

Verse 3

Fmaj7 Em7 Dm7 G
But I love you best,

Dm7 G
It's not something that I say in jest,

Dm7 G
'Cause you're different, girl, from all the rest,

Cmaj7 C7
In my eyes.

Fmaj7 Em7 Am7 D6
And I ran out be - fore but I won't do it any - more,

Dm7 G Cmaj7 Dm7
Can't you see the light in my eyes.___

Cmaj7 Dm7
In my eyes.___

Outro

Cmaj7 Dm7
In my eyes.

Cmaj7 Dm7
In my eyes. *To fade*

I'm Not In Love

Words & Music by Eric Stewart & Graham Gouldman

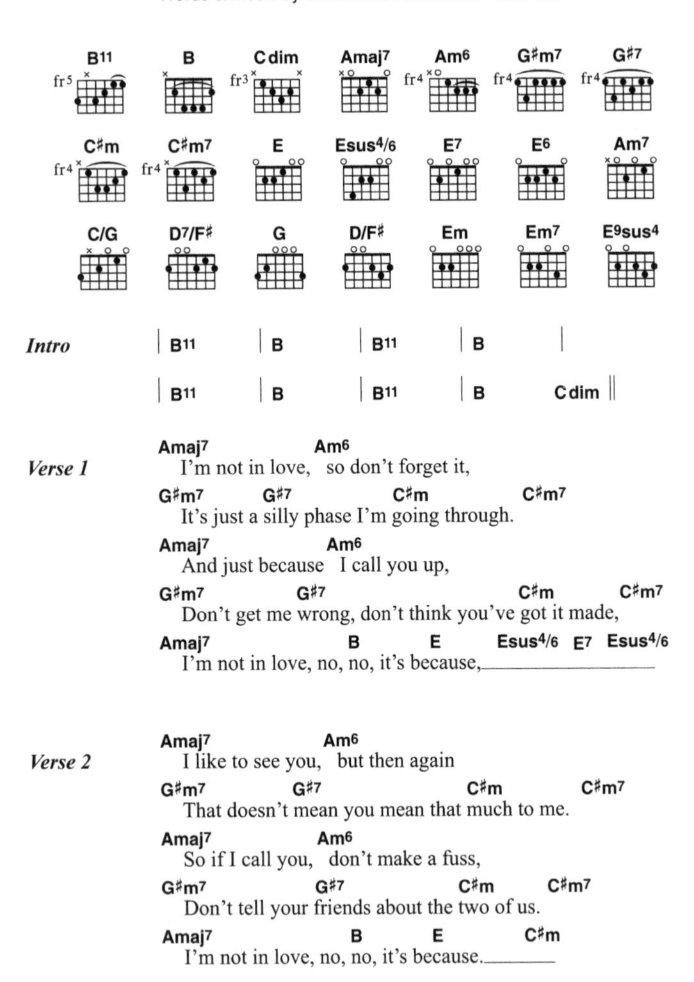

Intro | B11 | B | B11 | B |
| B11 | B | B11 | B Cdim ||

Verse 1

Amaj7 Am6
I'm not in love, so don't forget it,

G#m7 G#7 C#m C#m7
It's just a silly phase I'm going through.

Amaj7 Am6
And just because I call you up,

G#m7 G#7 C#m C#m7
Don't get me wrong, don't think you've got it made,

Amaj7 B E Esus4/6 E7 Esus4/6
I'm not in love, no, no, it's because,______________________

Verse 2

Amaj7 Am6
I like to see you, but then again

G#m7 G#7 C#m C#m7
That doesn't mean you mean that much to me.

Amaj7 Am6
So if I call you, don't make a fuss,

G#m7 G#7 C#m C#m7
Don't tell your friends about the two of us.

Amaj7 B E C#m
I'm not in love, no, no, it's because.___________

```
Link        | N.C.                    |
              E6
              (Be quiet, big boys don't cry,

              Big boys don't cry, big boys don't cry,
                                                     Cdim
              Big boys don't cry, big boys don't cry,)

            Amaj7                   Am6
Verse 3       I keep your picture   upon the wall,
            G#m7          G#7                C#m          C#m7
              It hides a nasty stain that's lying there.
            Amaj7                Am6
              So don't ask me    to give it back,
            G#m7                        G#7                   C#m          C#m7
              I know you know it doesn't mean that much to me.
            Amaj7                       B       E
              I'm not in love, no, no, it's because,

            Am7  C/G   D7/F#                   G    D/F#  Em  Em7
Bridge      Ooh, you'll wait a long time for me.
            Am7  C/G   D7/F#                E9sus4  E
            Ooh, you'll wait a long time.
            Am7  C/G   D7/F#                   G    D/F#  Em  Em7
            Ooh, you'll wait a long time for me.
            Am7  C/G   D7/F#                E9sus4  E
            Ooh, you'll wait a long time.

            Amaj7                Am6
Verse 4       I'm not in love,   so don't forget it,
            G#m7          G#7                C#m               C#m7
              It's just a silly phase I'm going through.
            Amaj7                  Am6
              And just because     I call you up,
            G#m7                 G#7                         C#m             C#m7
              Don't get me wrong, don't think you've got it made,
            Amaj7               Am6
              I'm not in love,  I'm not in love...

            |: B11        | B          :|  Repeat to fade
```

It Must Have Been Love

Words & Music by Per Gessle

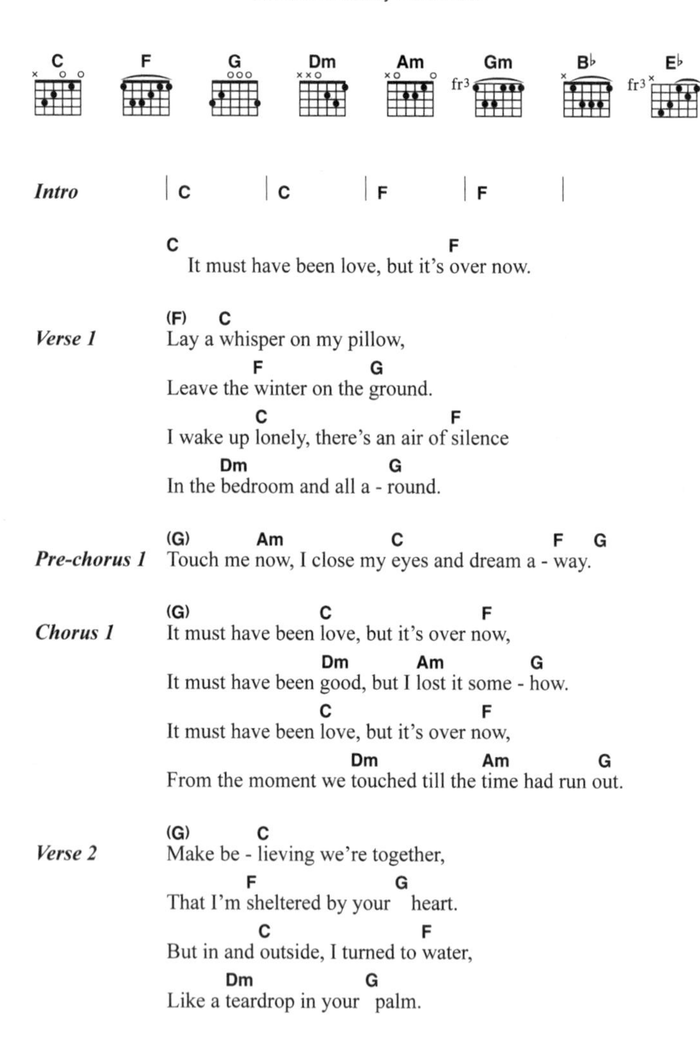

Intro | C | C | F | F |

C F
It must have been love, but it's over now.

Verse 1

(F) C
Lay a whisper on my pillow,
F G
Leave the winter on the ground.
C F
I wake up lonely, there's an air of silence
Dm G
In the bedroom and all a - round.

Pre-chorus 1

(G) Am C F G
Touch me now, I close my eyes and dream a - way.

Chorus 1

(G) C F
It must have been love, but it's over now,
Dm Am G
It must have been good, but I lost it some - how.
C F
It must have been love, but it's over now,
Dm Am G
From the moment we touched till the time had run out.

Verse 2

(G) C
Make be - lieving we're together,
F G
That I'm sheltered by your heart.
C F
But in and outside, I turned to water,
Dm G
Like a teardrop in your palm.

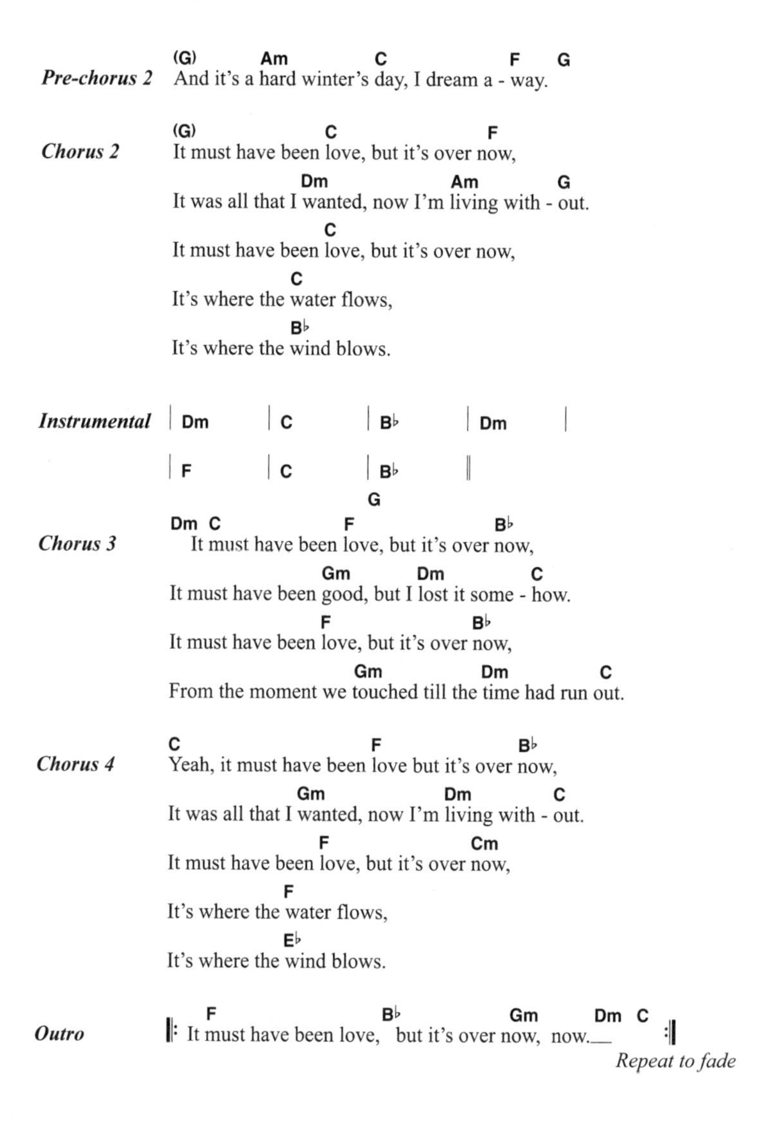

Pre-chorus 2

(G) Am C F G
And it's a hard winter's day, I dream a - way.

Chorus 2

(G) C F
It must have been love, but it's over now,
Dm Am G
It was all that I wanted, now I'm living with - out.
C
It must have been love, but it's over now,
C
It's where the water flows,
B♭
It's where the wind blows.

Instrumental

| Dm | C | B♭ | Dm |
| F | C | B♭ ‖

Chorus 3

Dm C G F B♭
It must have been love, but it's over now,
Gm Dm C
It must have been good, but I lost it some - how.
F B♭
It must have been love, but it's over now,
Gm Dm C
From the moment we touched till the time had run out.

Chorus 4

C F B♭
Yeah, it must have been love but it's over now,
Gm Dm C
It was all that I wanted, now I'm living with - out.
F Cm
It must have been love, but it's over now,
F
It's where the water flows,
E♭
It's where the wind blows.

Outro

F B♭ Gm Dm C
𝄆 It must have been love, but it's over now, now.__ 𝄇

Repeat to fade

Jack And Diane

Words & Music by John Mellencamp

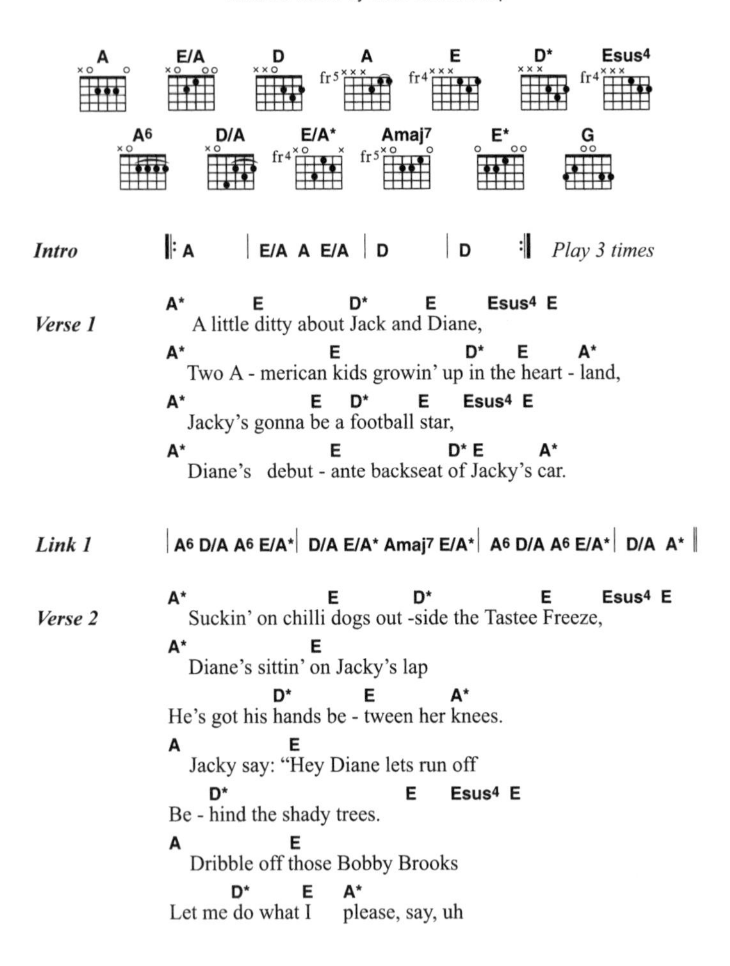

Chorus 1

```
A Aadd9 A  E    D        E
          "Oh yeah life goes on
A Aadd9 A        E        D       E     Esus4 E
  Long   after the thrill of livin' is gone, they   say
A Aadd9 A  E    D        E
          Oh yeah life goes on
A Aadd9  A        E        D    E A
  Long    after the thrill of livin' is gone"
```

They walk on.

Link 2

```
|: A     | E/A  A  E/A | D      | D     :|
```

Verse 3

```
A*              E                    D*              E    Esus4 E
  Jack, he sits back, collects his thoughts for a mo - ment,
A*               E                     D*  E    A*
  Scratches his head and does his best James Dean.
A*              E                           D*           E    Esus4 E
  "Well man, me and Diane, we oughta run off to the city."
A*               E                 D*    E   A
  Diane    says, "Baby, you ain't missin' no - thing."
```

And Jack, he say, ah:

Chorus 2

```
A*    E    D*       E
  "Oh yeah life goes on
A*                E       D*      E     Esus4 E
  Long after the thrill of livin' is gone,
A*    E                  D*      E
  Oh yeah, well they say life goes on
A*                     E      D*   E A
  Long after the thrill of livin' is gone."
```

(Harmony on bridge is implied by vocals, no chords played on guitar)

```
            A              D
*Bridge*    Gonna let it rock,
                       E*
            Let it roll,
            A*              D                    G          D
            Let the Bible Belt come and save my soul.
            A*             D            G               D
            Hold on to sixteen as long as you can,
            A*                                    D
            Changes come around real soon
                         E*               A
            Make us women and men.
```

Link 3 | A6 D/A A6 E/A | D/A E/A* Amaj7 E/A* | A6 D/A A6 E/A | D/A A* ‖

```
            A*              E       D*            E
*Chorus 3*    Oh yeah life goes on
            A*                         E          D*          E        Esus4  E
              Long after the thrill of livin' is gone.
            A*                  E                                D*          E
              Oh yeah, well they say life goes on
            A*                         E          D*    E  A*
              Long after the thrill of livin' is gone.
```

```
            A*                E/A              D/A          E/A
*Outro*       A little ditty about Jack and Diane,
            A*                          E/A                     D/A          A*
              Two American kids doing the best they can.
```

‖: A E/A | A E/A A E/A | D | D :‖ *Repeat to fade*

Labelled With Love

Words & Music by Chris Difford & Glen Tilbrook

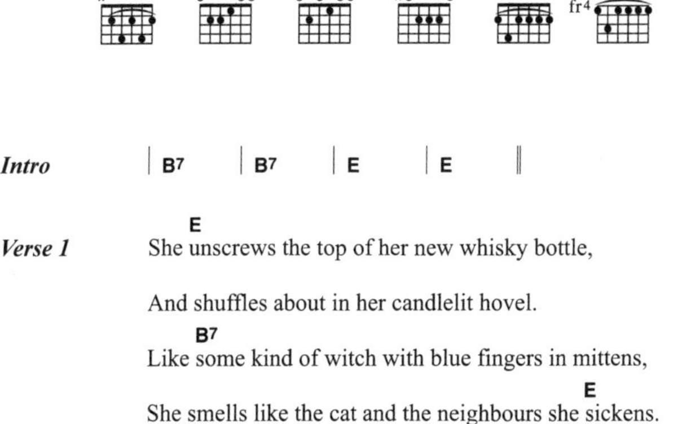

Intro | B7 | B7 | E | E ||

Verse 1

```
    E
She unscrews the top of her new whisky bottle,

And shuffles about in her candlelit hovel.
     B7
Like some kind of witch with blue fingers in mittens,
                                               E
She smells like the cat and the neighbours she sickens.

The black and white T.V. has long seen a picture,
    E7                     A
The cross on the wall is a permanent fixture.
    B7
The postman delivers the final reminders,
                               A         E
She sells off her silver and poodles in china.
```

Chorus 1

```
E                    F♯m7
Drinks to remember I, me and myself,
    B7                                        E
And winds up the clock and knocks dust from the shelf.
                    F♯m7
Home is a love that I miss very much,
        B7                             A   G♯m7 F♯m7 E
So, the past has been bottled and la - belled with  love.
```

Verse 2

E
During the wartime an American pilot
B7
Made every air raid a time of ex - citement.

She moved to his prairie and married the Texan,
E
She learnt from a distance how love was a lesson.

He became drinker and she became mother,
E7 A
She knew that one day she'd be one or the other.
B7
He ate himself older and drunk himself dizzy,
A E
Proud of her features she kept herself pretty.

Chorus 2

As Chorus 1

Verse 3

E
He like a cowboy died drunk in a slumber

Out on the porch in the middle of summer.
B7
She crossed the ocean back home to her family,
E
But they had retired to roads that were sandy.

She moved home alone without friends or relations,
E7 A
Lived in a world full of age reservations.
B7
On moth-eaten armchairs, she'd say that she'd sod all,
A G♯m7 F♯m7 E
To friends who had left her to drink from the bottle.

Chorus 3

```
E                           F♯m7
Drinks to remember I, me and myself,
     B7                                          E
And winds up the clock and knocks dust from the shelf.
                          F♯m7
Home is a love that I miss very much,
       B7                          A   G♯m7 F♯m7 E
So, the past has been bottled and la - belled with  love.
E                            F♯m7
Drinks to remember I, me and myself,
     B7                                          E
And winds up the clock and knocks dust from the shelf.
                          F♯m7
Home is a love that I miss very much,
       B7                          A   G♯m7 F♯m7 E
So, the past has been bottled and la - belled with  love.
```

Outro

```
    B7                          A   G♯m7 F♯m7 E
The past has been bottled and la - belled with  love.
    B7                          A   G♯m7 F♯m7 E
The past has been bottled and la - belled with  love.
```

```
|: E      | F♯m7  | B7    | E                  |
|  E      | F♯m7  | B7    | A G♯m7 F♯m7 E     :|
```
Repeat to fade

Livin' Thing

Words & Music by Jeff Lynne

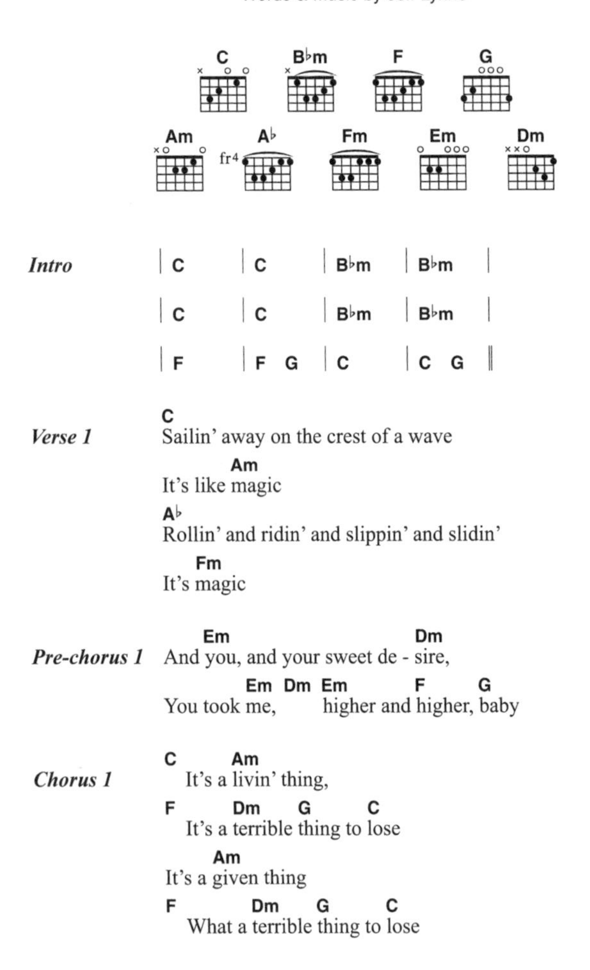

Intro

C	C	B♭m	B♭m
C	C	B♭m	B♭m
F	F G	C	C G	

Verse 1

C
Sailin' away on the crest of a wave
Am
It's like magic
A♭
Rollin' and ridin' and slippin' and slidin'
Fm
It's magic

Pre-chorus 1

Em Dm
And you, and your sweet de - sire,
Em Dm Em F G
You took me, higher and higher, baby

Chorus 1

C Am
It's a livin' thing,
F Dm G C
It's a terrible thing to lose
Am
It's a given thing
F Dm G C
What a terrible thing to lose

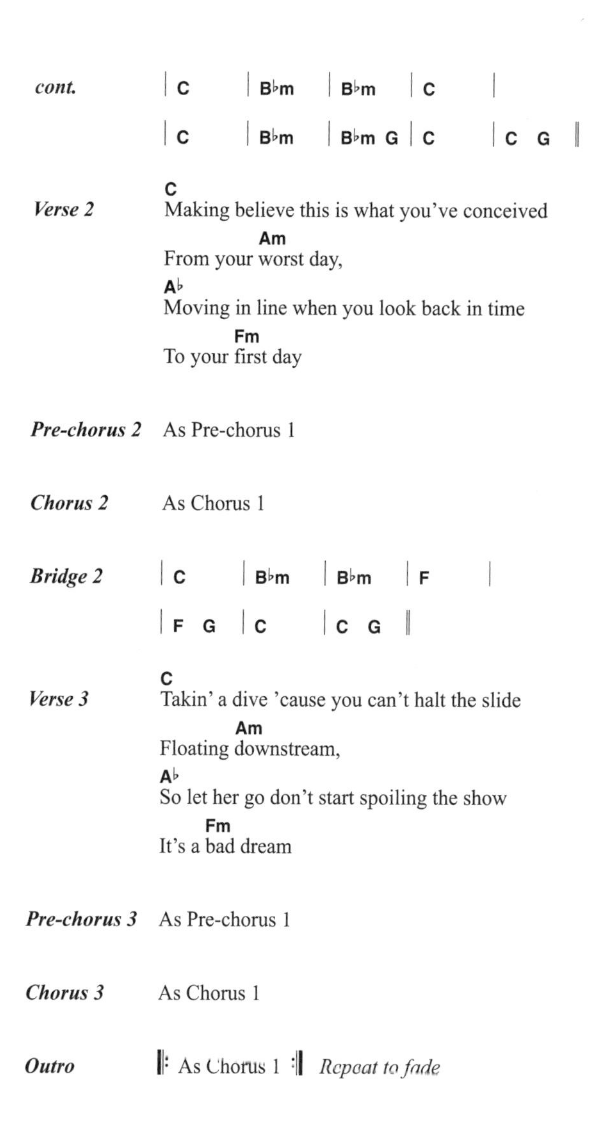

cont. | C | B♭m | B♭m | C |

| C | B♭m | B♭m G | C | C G ‖

Verse 2

C
Making believe this is what you've conceived
Am
From your worst day,
A♭
Moving in line when you look back in time
Fm
To your first day

Pre-chorus 2 As Pre-chorus 1

Chorus 2 As Chorus 1

Bridge 2 | C | B♭m | B♭m | F |

| F G | C | C G ‖

Verse 3

C
Takin' a dive 'cause you can't halt the slide
Am
Floating downstream,
A♭
So let her go don't start spoiling the show
Fm
It's a bad dream

Pre-chorus 3 As Pre-chorus 1

Chorus 3 As Chorus 1

Outro ‖: As Chorus 1 :‖ *Repeat to fade*

Living Doll

Words & Music by Lionel Bart

A   B7   E7   F♯   E   D   A6/9 (fr6)

Chorus 1

```
N.C.                A
Got myself a cryin', talkin', sleepin', walkin', livin' doll,
                                                        B7              E7
Gotta do my best to please her just 'cause she's a livin' doll.
              A                                          F♯
Got a rovin' eye and that is why she satisfies my soul,
                     A             E             A
Got the one and only, walkin', talkin', livin' doll.
```

Bridge 1

```
N.C.                         D
Well, take a look at her hair, it's real
                              A
And if you don't be - lieve what I say, just feel.
                   D
Gonna lock her up in a trunk,
                        E     N.C.
So no big hunk can steal her away from me.
```

Chorus 2 As Chorus 1

Interlude

A	A	A	A
A	A	B7	E7
A	A	F♯	F♯
A	E	A	A N.C.

Bridge 2 As Bridge 1

Chorus 3

```
N.C.          A
Got myself a cryin', talkin', sleepin', walkin', livin' doll,
                                                B7        E7
Gotta do my best to please her just 'cause she's a livin' doll.
              A                                   F#
Got a rovin' eye and that is why she satisfies my soul,
                A           E       N.C.     A6/9
Got the one and only, walkin', talkin', livin' doll.
```

The Loco-Motion

Words & Music by Gerry Goffin & Carole King

E♭5 E♭ Cm A♭ Fm F/A B♭7

Intro | E♭5 | E♭5 | E♭5 | E♭5 ||

Verse 1

```
E♭                          Cm
Everybody is doing a brand new dance, now.
E♭                       Cm
   (Come on baby, do the Loco-motion).
  E♭                                   Cm
I know you'll get to like it if you give it a chance now.
E♭                       Cm
   (Come on baby, do the Loco-motion).
    A♭                         Fm
My little baby sister can do it with me,
    A♭                               F/A
It's easier than learning your A, B, C.
   E♭                        B♭7                        (E♭)
So come on, come on, do the Loco-motion with me.
```

Bridge 1

```
E♭
   You gotta swing your hips, now,
A♭
   Come on, baby.
      E♭
Jump up, jump back,
               B♭7
Ooh, well, I think you've got the knack.
```

Verse 2

```
E♭                            Cm
Now that you can do it, let's make a chain, now.
E♭                       Cm
   (Come on baby, do the Loco-motion).
  E♭                                 Cm
A chug-a chug-a motion like a railroad train, now.
E♭                       Cm
   (Come on baby, do the Loco-motion).
```

cont.

A♭ Fm
Do it nice and easy, now, don't lose control,
A♭ F/A
A little bit of rhythm and a lot of soul.
E♭ B♭7 (E♭)
Come on, come on, do the Loco-motion with me.

Instrumental

| E♭ | E♭ | A♭ | A♭ |
| E♭ | E♭ | B♭7 ‖

B♭7
Yeah, yeah, yeah, yeah.

Verse 3

E♭ Cm
Move around the floor in a Loco-motion.
E♭ Cm
(Come on baby, do the Loco-motion).
E♭ Cm
Do it holding hands if you do get the notion.
E♭ Cm
(Come on baby, do the Loco-motion).
A♭ Fm
There's never been a dance that's so easy to do,
A♭ F/A
It even makes you happy when you're feeling blue.
E♭ B♭7 (E♭)
So come on, come on, do the Loco-motion with me.

Outro

E♭
You gotta swing your hips, now,
A♭ E♭
That's right, you're doing fine.
A♭
Come on, baby.
E♭
Mmm, Jump up, jump back,
A♭
You're looking good.
E♭
Mmm, Jump up, jump back. *To fade*

The Look Of Love

From CASINO ROYALE
Words by Hal David
Music by Burt Bacharach

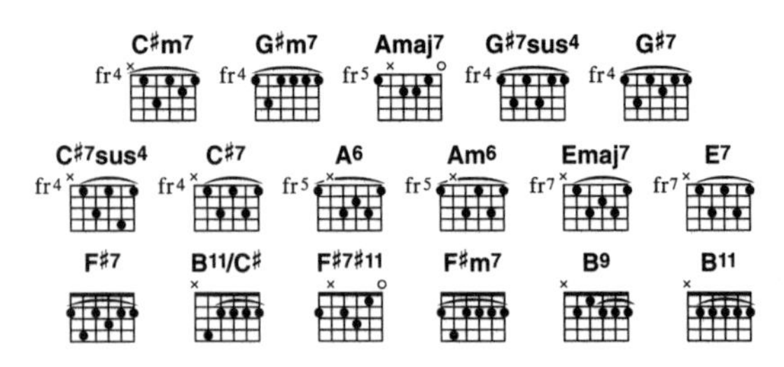

Verse 1

C♯m7 G♯m7
The look of love is in your eyes,
Amaj7 G♯7sus4 G♯7
A look your smile can't dis - guise.
C♯m7 C♯7sus4 C♯7
The look of love,
A6 Am6 Emaj7 E7
It's saying so much more than just words could ever say,
Amaj7 G♯7sus4 C♯m7 F♯7
And what my heart has heard, well, it takes my breath a - way.

Bridge 1

(F♯7) Emaj7 B11/C♯
I can hardly wait to hold you, feel my arms around you.

How long I have waited,
Emaj7 B11/C♯
Waited just to love you, now that I have found you.

Verse 2

(B11/C♯) C♯m7 G♯m7
You've got the look of love, it's on your face,
Amaj7 G♯7sus4 G♯7
A look that time can't e - rase.
C♯m7 C♯7sus4 C♯7
Be mine to - night,
A6 Am6 Emaj7 E7
Let this be just the start of so many nights like this,
Amaj7 G♯7sus4 C♯m7 F♯7
Let's take a lover's vow and then seal it with a kiss.

Bridge 2

(F#7) Emaj7 B11/C#
I can hardly wait to hold you, feel my arms around you.

How long I have waited,

Emaj7 B11/C#
Waited just to love you, now that I have found you,

C#m7 F#7#11
Don't ever go, don't ever go,

F#m7 B9 Emaj7
I love you so.

Instrumental

C#m7	C#m7	G#m7	G#m7
Amaj7	Amaj7	G#7sus4	G#7
C#m7	C#7sus4 C#7	A6	Am6
Am6	Emaj7 E7	Amaj7	Amaj7
G#7sus4	C#m7 F#7
Emaj7	B11/C#	B11/C#	B11/C#
Emaj7	B11/C#	B11/C#
C#m7	C#m7	F#7#11	F#7#11
F#m7	F#m7 B11	Emaj7	N.C.
C#m7	C#m7	G#m7	G#m7
Amaj7	Amaj7	G#7sus4	G#7
C#m7	C#7sus4 C#7		*To fade*

Love Shack

Words & Music by Fred Schneider, Kate Pierson, Cynthia Wilson & Keith Strickland

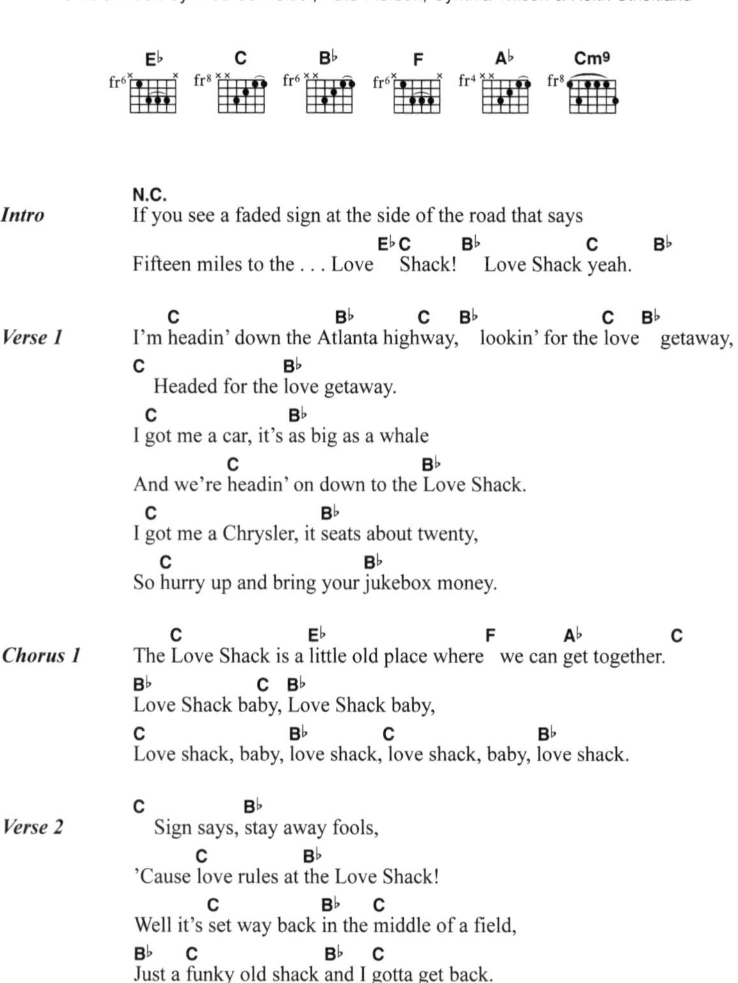

cont.

C   B♭
Glitter on the mattress,
C   B♭
Glitter on the highway,
C   B♭
Glitter on the front porch,
C   B♭
Glitter on the hallway.

Chorus 2

    C   E♭   F   A♭   C
The Love Shack is a little old place where   we can get together.
B♭   C B♭   C   B♭
Love Shack baby! Love Shack baby! Love Shack, that's where it's at!
C   B♭
Love Shack, that's where it's at!

Verse 3

C   B♭
Huggin' and a kissin', dancin' and a lovin',
C   B♭
Wearin' next to nothing 'cause it's hot as an oven
    C   B♭
The whole shack shimmies when everybody's movin'
  C   E♭
Around and around and around and around.
C   B♭
Everybody's movin', everybody's groovin' baby!
C   B♭
Folks linin' up outside just to get down.
C   B♭
Everybody's movin', everybody's groovin' baby!
C   B♭
Funky little shack! Funky little shack!

Link

| C | B♭ | C | B♭ |

Verse 4

C   B♭   C   B♭
Hop in my Chrysler, it's as big as a whale and it's about to set sail!
 C   B♭
I got me a car, it seats about twenty,
        C   B♭
So come on and bring your jukebox money.

Chorus 3

```
    C               E♭                      F       A♭          C
The Love Shack is a little old place where  we can get together.
B♭              C  B♭
Love shack baby, love shack baby,
C                B♭
Love shack, baby, love shack,
C                B♭
Love shack, baby, love shack.
```

Middle

```
| C       | B♭      | C       | B♭      |
```

```
C                B♭                 C
Bang bang bang on the door baby!
B♭
Knock a little louder sugar!
C                B♭                 C
Bang bang bang on the door baby!
B♭
I can't hear you!
Cm9        B♭
Bang bang, on the door baby,
Cm9        B♭
Bang bang, on the door.
Cm9        B♭
Bang bang, on the door baby,
Cm9    B♭         C     N.C.
Bang bang, you're what? . . . Tin roof, rusted!
```

Outro

```
C                B♭
Love Shack, baby Love Shack!
C                B♭
Love Shack, baby Love Shack!
C                B♭
Love Shack, baby Love Shack!
C                B♭              C
Love Shack, baby Love Shack!
```

Maggie May

Words & Music by Rod Stewart & Martin Quittenton

D Em7 G A Em F♯m Asus4

Intro

| D | Em7 | G | D G |

| D | Em7 | G | D G ‖

Verse 1

```
A                  G                        D
Wake up Maggie, I think I got something to say to you,
   A                     G                D
It's late September and I really should be back at school.
 G                D
I know I keep you amused
    G            A
But I feel I'm being used,
   Em                        F♯m      Em
Oh, Maggie, I couldn't have tried any more.
Asus4 Em              A
  You  lured me away from home
        Em              A
Just to save you from being alone,
    Em                 A         D
You stole my heart and that's what really hurts.
```

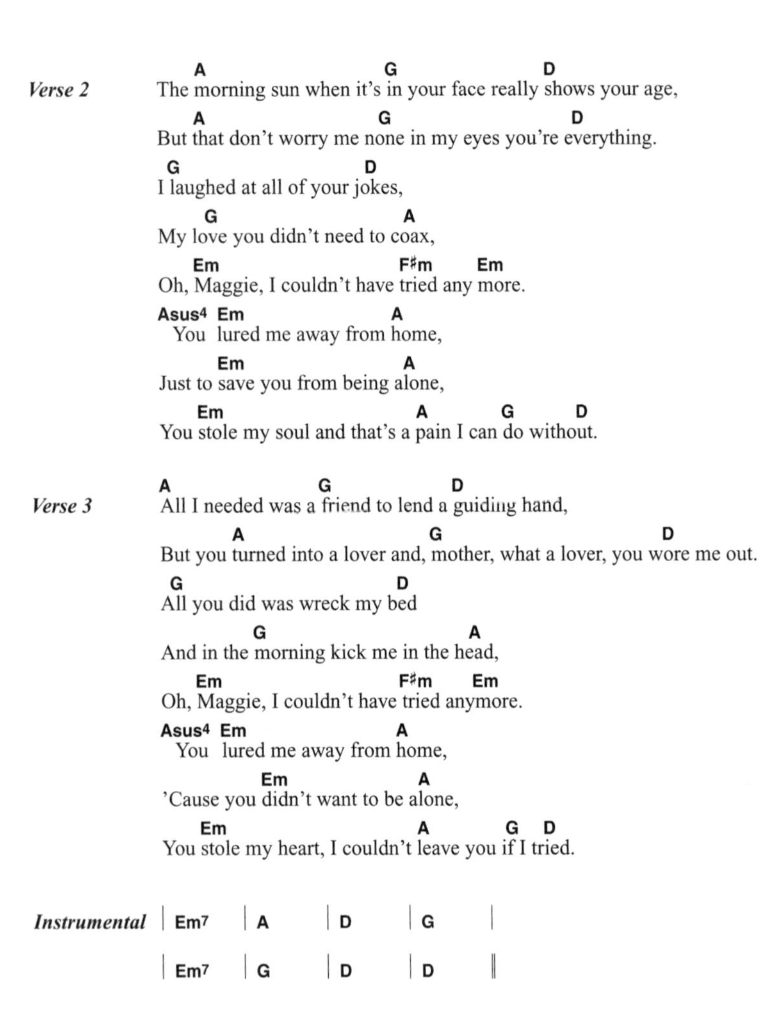

Verse 2

A G D
The morning sun when it's in your face really shows your age,
A G D
But that don't worry me none in my eyes you're everything.
G D
I laughed at all of your jokes,
G A
My love you didn't need to coax,
Em F♯m Em
Oh, Maggie, I couldn't have tried any more.
Asus4 Em A
You lured me away from home,
Em A
Just to save you from being alone,
Em A G D
You stole my soul and that's a pain I can do without.

Verse 3

A G D
All I needed was a friend to lend a guiding hand,
A G D
But you turned into a lover and, mother, what a lover, you wore me out.
G D
All you did was wreck my bed
G A
And in the morning kick me in the head,
Em F♯m Em
Oh, Maggie, I couldn't have tried anymore.
Asus4 Em A
You lured me away from home,
Em A
'Cause you didn't want to be alone,
Em A G D
You stole my heart, I couldn't leave you if I tried.

Instrumental | Em7 | A | D | G |

| Em7 | G | D | D ||

```
           A                   G                    D
Verse 4    I suppose I could collect my books and get on back to school,
             A                  G                      D
           Or steal my daddy's cue and make a living out of playing pool.
             G                           D
           Or find myself a rock and roll band,
              G              A
           That needs a helpin' hand,
              Em                F♯m              Em
           Oh, Maggie, I wished I'd never seen your face.
           Asus4       Em                 A
             You made a first class fool out of me,
                     Em              A
           But I'm as blind as a fool can be,
              Em                  A         G   D
           You stole my heart but I love you anyway.


Instrumental | Em7  | A    | D    | G    |

             | Em7  | G    | D    | D    ||

             | Em7  | A    | D    | G    |

             | Em7  | G    |

             |: D   | Em7  | G    | D   :|  Play five times

           D       Em7     G            D
Outro      Maggie I wish I'd never seen your face,

           | D    | Em7  | G    | D    |
              D              Em7 G           D
           I'll get on back home   one of these days.

           |: D   | Em7  | G    | D   :|  Repeat to fade, vocal ad lib.
```

Mercy

Words & Music by Aimee Duffy & Stephen Booker

Intro

‖: (G) | (G) :‖

(G) (C/G) (G7) (C/G)
‖: Yeah, yeah, yeah,
(G) (C/G) (G7) (C/G)
Yeah, yeah, yeah. :‖

| Dm7 | C |

| G7 | G7 |

Verse 1

G7
I love you,

But I gotta stay true.

My moral's got me on my knees,

I'm begging please,

Stop playing games.

Pre-Chorus 1

Dm7
I don't know what this is,
C
But you got me good,
G7
Just like you knew you would.
Dm7
I don't know what you do,
C
But you do it well,
G7
I'm under your spell.

Chorus 1

```
                                        G7
You got me begging you for mercy,

Why won't you release me?
                                        C
You got me begging you for mercy,
                              G7
Why won't you re - lease me?
                Dm7  C  G7
I said re - lease__ me.
```

Verse 2

```
G7
    Now you think that I,

Will be something on the side.

But you got to understand,

That I need a man,

Who can take my hand, yes I do.
```

Pre-Chorus 2 As Pre-Chorus 1

Chorus 2

```
                                        G7
You got me begging you for mercy,

Why won't you release me?
                                        C
You got me begging you for mercy,
                              G7
Why won't you re - lease me?
                                   Dm7      C        G7
I said you'd better re - lease me__ yeah.__
```

Bridge

N.C.
I'm begging you for mercy,

Just why won't you release me?

I'm begging you for mercy,

You got me begging,

You got me begging,

You got me begging.

Chorus 3

G7
Mercy, why won't you release me?

C
I'm begging you for mercy,

G7
Why won't you re - lease me?

Dm7 C G7
You've got me begging you for mer - cy, yeah.

I'm begging you for mercy,

I'm begging you for mercy,

C
I'm begging you for mercy,

G7
I'm begging you for mercy.

Dm7 C G7
Why won't you re - lease__ me, yeah?

Outro

G7
‖: You've got me begging you for mercy,

You got me begging,

Down on my knees. :‖ *repeat ad lib. to fade*

Mr. Jones

Words by Adam Duritz
Music by Adam Duritz & David Bryson

Am F Dm G C Gsus4 Fsus2 Fmaj7

```
Intro     | Am  | F   | Dm  | G   | Am  | F   | G   | G   |

           Am                              F
Verse 1      I was down at the New Amsterdam
           Dm                  G
             Staring at this yellow-haired girl,
               Am                        F           G
           Mr. Jones strikes up a conversation with a black-haired flamenco dancer.
                       Am                   F               Dm
           You know she dances while his father plays guitar
                                G
           She's suddenly beautiful.
                     Am                     F
           And we all want something beautiful
           G
             Man, I wish I was beautiful.

              Am                             F
Verse 2    So come dance this silence down through the morning,
           Dm      G            Am      F
             Sha la la la la la la la, yeah.
           G
             Uh huh, yeah.
           Am           F
             Cut up, Maria!
           Dm                            G                 Am
             Show me some of them Spanish dances, and
                       F          G
           Pass me a bottle, Mr. Jones.
           Am           F
             Believe in me,
           Dm                      G
             Help me believe in anything,
                  Am          F                G
           'Cause I wanna be someone who believes, yeah.
```

Chorus 1

```
C     F            G                    Gsus4
   Mr. Jones and me   tell each other fairy tales
G  C                       F        Fsus2
And we stare at the beautiful women.
 F   G                                        C
"She's looking at you. Ah no, no, she's looking at me."
                 F             Fsus2 F
Smiling in the bright lights,
G                              Gsus4
   Coming through in stereo.
G     C            Fsus2 F    G
When everybody loves   you,   you can never be lonely.
```

Verse 3

```
      Am                F
Well I'm gonna paint my picture,
Dm              G                         Am
   Paint myself in blue and red and black and grey,
                        F                G
All of the beautiful colours are very, very meaningful.
                       Am                  F
Yeah well you know grey is my favourite colour,
  Dm         G
I    felt so symbolic, yesterday,
Am           F
   If I knew Picasso,
         G                          C
I would buy myself a grey guitar and play.
```

Chorus 2

```
    F            G                    Gsus4
Mr. Jones and me   look into the future,
G     C                     F         Fsus2
Yeah, we stare at the beautiful women,
 F   G                                               C
"She's looking at you. I don't think so. She's looking at me."
                  F          Fsus2  F
Standing in the spotlight,
G                                  Gsus4
   I bought myself a grey guitar.
G     C          F         G                     Am
When everybody loves me,   I will never be lonely.
```

```
                      Fmaj7
Middle      I will never be lonely,

                        Am             G
            Said I'm never gonna be, lonely.
            Am
              I wanna be a lion,
            Fmaj7
            And everybody wants to pass as cats,
            Am
              We all want to be big, big stars, yeah but
            G
              We got different reasons for that.
            Am                          Fmaj7
              Believe in me, because I don't believe in anything
                Am                           G
            And I, I wanna be someone to believe,  to believe, to believe, yeah.

            C    F          G                            Gsus4
Chorus 3      Mr. Jones and me   stumbling through the barrio
            G    C                   F
            Yeah, we stare at the beautiful women,
                 G                                              C
            "She's perfect for you, man, there's got to be somebody for me."
                           F       Fsus2
            I want to be Bob Dylan,
            F  G                                      Gsus4 G
            Mr. Jones wishes he was someone just a little more  funky
            C                     F         Fsus2 F G
            And then everybody loves you,          oh son,

            That's just about as funky as you can be.

            C    F     Fsus2 F  Gsus4 G                    Gsus4
Chorus 4      Mr. Jones and   me         staring at the video,
            G     C              F      Fsus2 F    G
            When I look at the television I      want to see me staring

            Right back at me.
            C                      F  Fsus2  F     G
              We all want to be big stars,   but we don't know why and we

            Don't know how
                        C          F          Fsus2
            But when everybody loves me
            F      G
            I wanna be just about as happy as I can be.
            C    F          G
              Mr. Jones and me:  we're gonna be big stars.
```

More Than This

Words & Music by Bryan Ferry

```
Intro      ‖: C♯       | C♯       | C♯sus4    | C♯sus4  :‖

                     F♯           B
Verse 1    I could feel at the time
                          G♯m    C♯
           There was no way of knowing
                  F♯              B
           Fallen leaves in the night
                     G♯m                 C♯
           Who can say where they're blowing
              F♯          B
           As free as the wind
           G♯m       C♯
           Hopefully learning
                     F♯          B
           Why the sea on the tide
                G♯m        C♯
           Has no way of turning

                          F♯                   B
Chorus 1   More than this you know there's nothing
                          F♯       B
           More than this tell me one thing
                          F♯        B
           More than this there is nothing

Link 1     | C♯       | C♯       | B        | B        ‖
```

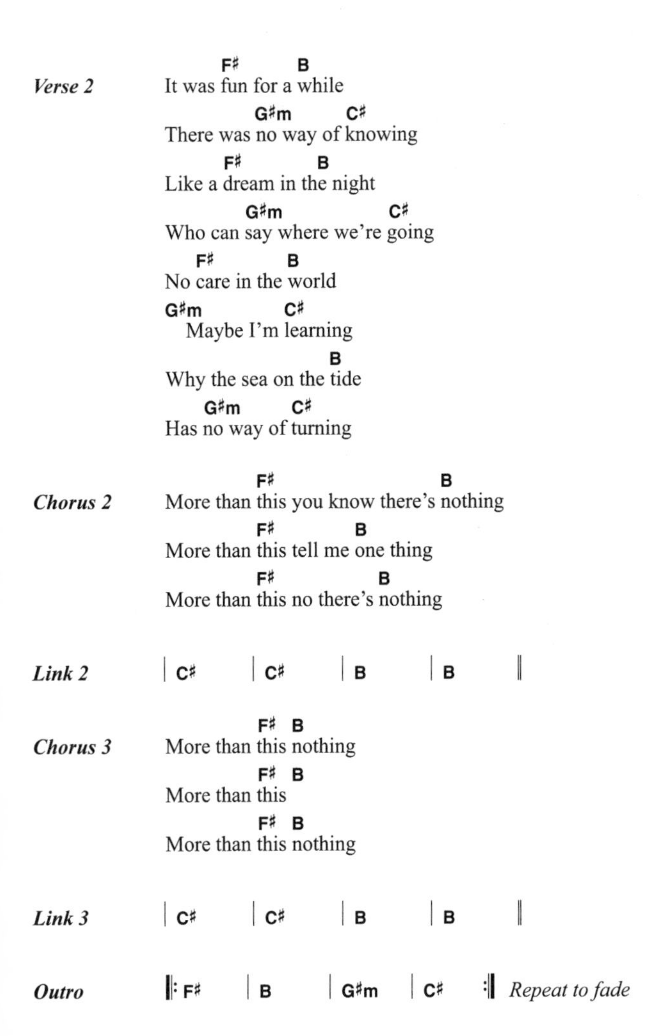

Verse 2

F♯ B
It was fun for a while
G♯m C♯
There was no way of knowing
F♯ B
Like a dream in the night
G♯m C♯
Who can say where we're going
F♯ B
No care in the world
G♯m C♯
Maybe I'm learning
B
Why the sea on the tide
G♯m C♯
Has no way of turning

Chorus 2

F♯ B
More than this you know there's nothing
F♯ B
More than this tell me one thing
F♯ B
More than this no there's nothing

Link 2

| C♯ | C♯ | B | B ||

Chorus 3

F♯ B
More than this nothing
F♯ B
More than this
F♯ B
More than this nothing

Link 3

| C♯ | C♯ | B | B ||

Outro

‖: F♯ | B | G♯m | C♯ :‖ *Repeat to fade*

Mustang Sally

Words & Music by Bonny Rice

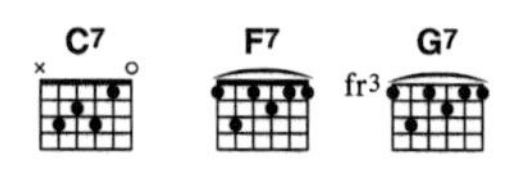

Intro | C7 | C7 | C7 | C7 ||

Verse 1

C7
Mustang Sally, huh, huh,

Guess you better slow your Mustang down.

Oh Lord, what I say now.

F7
Mustang Sally, now baby, oh Lord,

C7
Guess you better slow your Mustang down.

Huh, oh yeah.

G7 F7
You been runnin' all over town, now,

N.C. C7
Oh, I guess I have to put your flat feet on the ground.

Ha, what I said, now, listen.

Chorus 1

C7
All you wanna do is ride around Sally.

(Ride Sally, ride)

All you wanna do is ride around Sally.

(Ride Sally, ride)

F7
All you wanna do is ride around Sally.

(Ride Sally ride) huh.

```
              C7
cont.         All you wanna do is a-ride around Sally, oh Lord.

              (Ride Sally ride)

              Well, listen here.
              G7                               F7
              One of these early mornings, yeah,
              N.C.                                C7
              Wow, gonna be wiping your weeping eyes, huh.

              What I said, now, look-a-here,

              C7
Verse 2       I bought you a brand new Mustang,

              A nineteen sixty-five, huh.

              Now you come around, signifying woman

              You don't wanna let me ride.
                     F7
              Mustang___ Sally, now baby, oh Lord,
                                             C7
              Guess you better slow that Mustang down, huh, oh Lord.
                                G7                     F7
              Listen, you been running all over town.
              N.C.                                   C7
              Ow, I got to put your flat feet on the ground, huh.

              What I said now, yeah.

              Let me say it one more time y'all.

              C7
Chorus 2      Now, all you wanna do is ride around Sally.

              (Ride Sally ride)

              All you wanna do is ride around Sally.

              (Ride, Sally ride)   To fade
```

My Cherie Amour

Words & Music by Stevie Wonder, Henry Cosby & Sylvia Moy

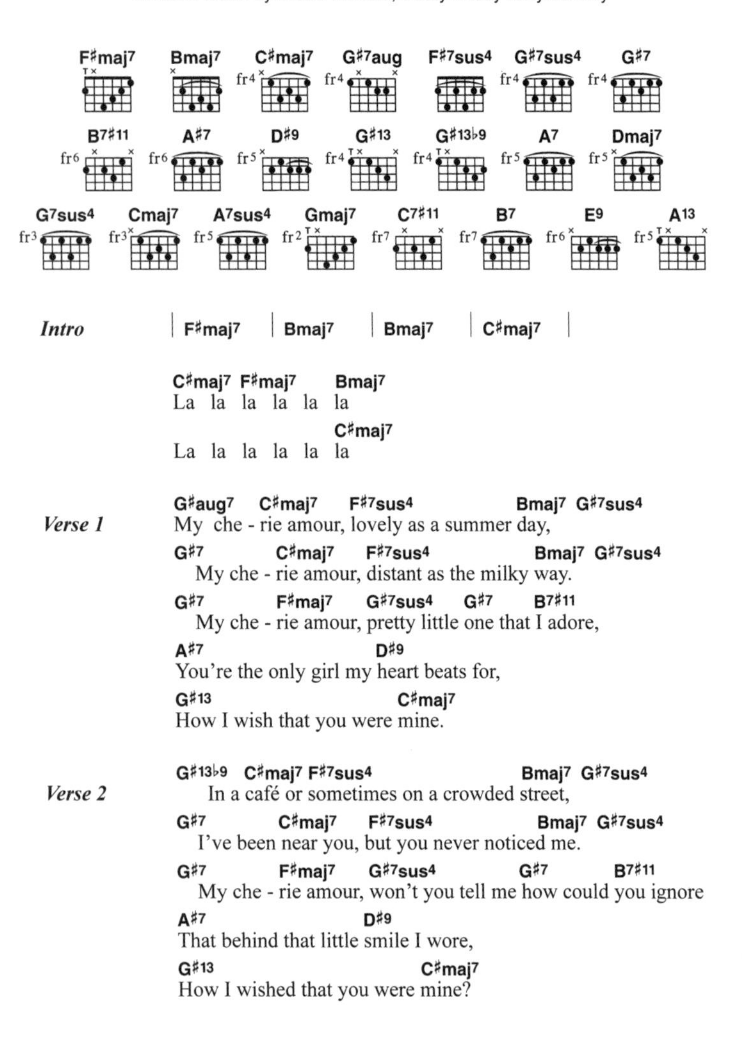

Bridge 1

```
C#maj7 F#maj7     Bmaj7
La  la  la  la  la  la
                  C#maj7
La  la  la  la  la  la
       F#maj7     Bmaj7
La  la  la  la  la  la
                  C#maj7
La  la  la  la  la  la
```

Verse 3

```
A7      Dmaj7            G7sus4                  Cmaj7
Maybe someday, you'll see my face among the crowd,
A7sus4  A7     Dmaj7           G7sus4                Cmaj7
   May   -   be someday, I'll share your little distant cloud.
A7sus4  A7          Gmaj7       A7sus4              C7#11
        Oh, che - rie amour, pretty little one that I adore,
B7                          E9
You're the only girl my heart beats for,
A13                              Dmaj7
How I wish that you were mine.
```

Outro

```
Dmaj7  Gmaj7      Cmaj7
La  la  la  la  la  la
                  Dmaj7
La  la  la  la  la  la
       Gmaj7      Cmaj7
La  la  la  la  la  la
                  Dmaj7
La  la  la  la  la  la   To fade
```

My Girl

Words & Music by William "Smokey" Robinson & Ronald White

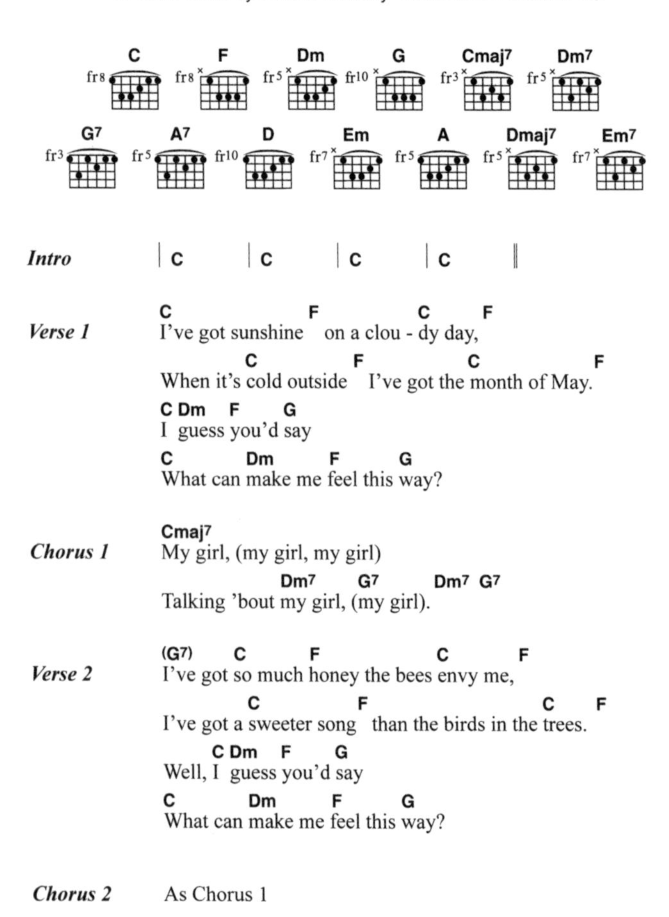

Intro | C | C | C | C ||

Verse 1

C F C F
I've got sunshine on a clou - dy day,
C F C F
When it's cold outside I've got the month of May.
C Dm F G
I guess you'd say
C Dm F G
What can make me feel this way?

Chorus 1

Cmaj7
My girl, (my girl, my girl)
Dm7 G7 Dm7 G7
Talking 'bout my girl, (my girl).

Verse 2

(G7) C F C F
I've got so much honey the bees envy me,
C F C F
I've got a sweeter song than the birds in the trees.
C Dm F G
Well, I guess you'd say
C Dm F G
What can make me feel this way?

Chorus 2 As Chorus 1

Link 1

```
| C        | C        | C        | C        |
Ooh, hoo.
```

Instrumental

```
| C        | F        | C        | F        |
             Hey, hey,  hey.      Hey, hey,

| Dm       | G7       | Em       | A7       ||
  Hey.                      Ooh,  yeah.
```

Verse 3

```
(A7)   D                  G         D       G
I don't need no money,    fortune, or fame,
           D                        G          D           G
I've got   all the riches baby,     one man    can claim.
          D Em   G      A
Well, I   guess you'll say
D          Em       G        A
What can make me feel this way?
```

Chorus 3

```
Dmaj7
My girl, (my girl, my girl)
                   Em7      A7
Talking, 'bout my girl, (my girl).
                  Dmaj7
(Talking 'bout my girl)
                                             Em7
I've got sunshine on a cloudy day with my girl.
     A7                                  Dmaj7
I've even got the month of May with my girl.
                   Em7
Talking, 'bout my girl.   To fade
```

Nowhere To Run

Words & Music by Brian Holland, Eddie Holland & Lamont Dozier

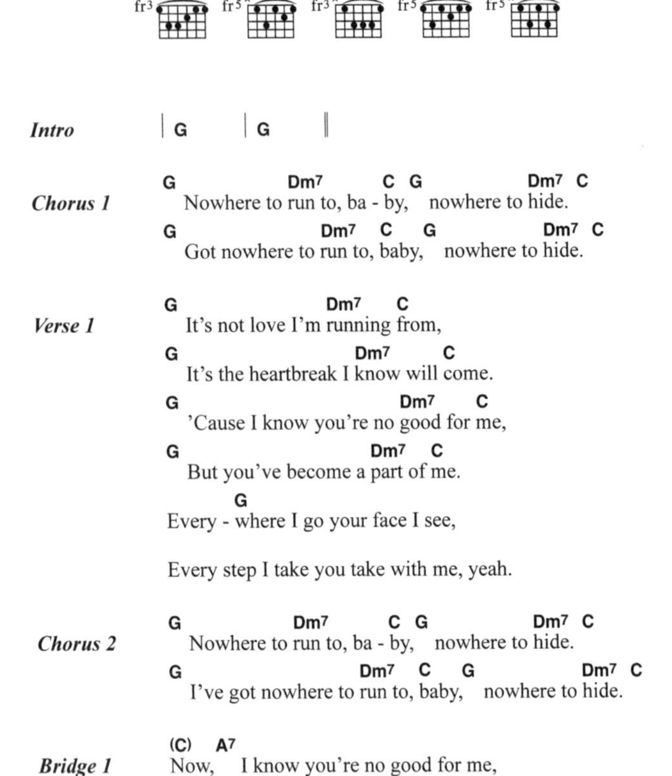

Intro | G | G ||

Chorus 1

G Dm7 C G Dm7 C
Nowhere to run to, ba - by, nowhere to hide.

G Dm7 C G Dm7 C
Got nowhere to run to, baby, nowhere to hide.

Verse 1

G Dm7 C
It's not love I'm running from,

G Dm7 C
It's the heartbreak I know will come.

G Dm7 C
'Cause I know you're no good for me,

G Dm7 C
But you've become a part of me.

G
Every - where I go your face I see,

Every step I take you take with me, yeah.

Chorus 2

G Dm7 C G Dm7 C
Nowhere to run to, ba - by, nowhere to hide.

G Dm7 C G Dm7 C
I've got nowhere to run to, baby, nowhere to hide.

Bridge 1

(C) A7
Now, I know you're no good for me,

D7 (G)
But free of you I'll never be, no.

Verse 2

```
G                  Dm7       C G          Dm7       C
  Each night as I sleep        into my heart you creep.
G                      Dm7   C
  I wake up feeling sorry I met you,
G                     Dm7    C
  Hoping soon that I'll for - get you.
      G
When I look in the mirror to comb my hair,

I see your face just a-smilin' there, yeah.
```

Chorus 3 As Chorus 2

Bridge 2

```
(C)    A7
  Now,  I know you're no good for me,
D7
  But you've become a part of me.
```

Verse 3

```
G                 Dm7       C G               Dm7 C
  How can I fight a love      that shouldn't be,
    G            Dm7 C   G               Dm7 C
When  it's so deep,  so deep,  deep inside of me.
    G
My love reaches so high you can't get over it,

It's so wide you can't get around it.
```

Chorus 4

```
G                  Dm7      C G              Dm7 C
  Nowhere to run to, ba - by,   nowhere to hide.
G                     Dm7            C    G                  Dm7 C
  I just can't get a - way from you baby,   no matter how I try.
```

Bridge 3 As Bridge 1

Chorus 5

```
G                  Dm7      C G              Dm7 C
  Nowhere to run to, ba - by,   nowhere to hide.
G                         Dm7  C   G               Dm7 C
  I've got nowhere to run to, baby,   nowhere to hide.
G                         Dm7 C           G              Dm7 C
  I've got nowhere to run,  nowhere to hide from you baby.  To fade
```

Orinoco Flow

Words by Roma Ryan
Music by Enya

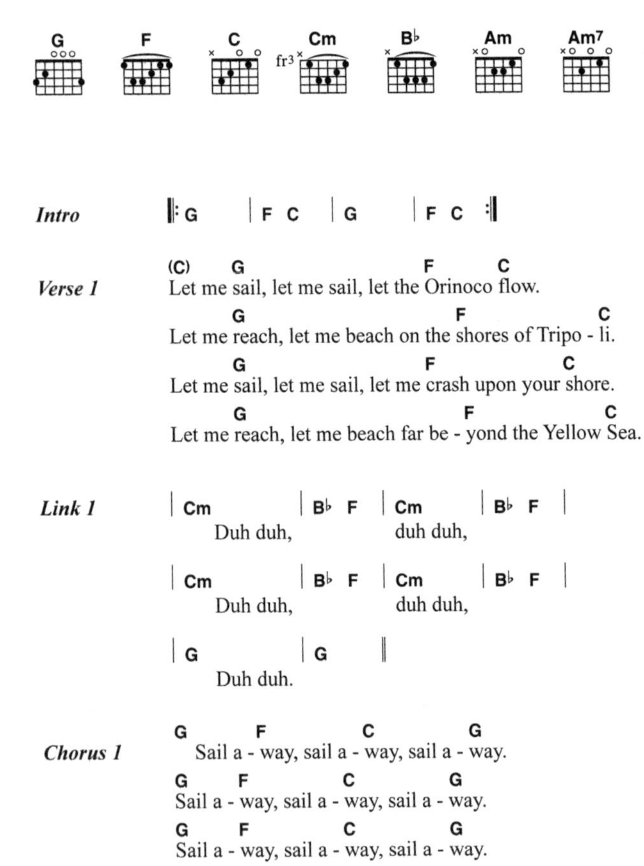

Intro

𝄆 G | F C | G | F C 𝄇

Verse 1

```
(C)     G                             F          C
Let me sail, let me sail, let the Orinoco flow.
        G                              F                  C
Let me reach, let me beach on the shores of Tripo - li.
        G                          F                    C
Let me sail, let me sail, let me crash upon your shore.
        G                                   F                  C
Let me reach, let me beach far be - yond the Yellow Sea.
```

Link 1

```
| Cm           | B♭ F | Cm          | B♭ F |
    Duh duh,            duh duh,
| Cm           | B♭ F | Cm          | B♭ F |
    Duh duh,            duh duh,
| G            | G      ||
    Duh duh.
```

Chorus 1

```
G        F               C               G
   Sail a - way, sail a - way, sail a - way.
G        F            C              G
Sail a - way, sail a - way, sail a - way.
G        F            C              G
Sail a - way, sail a - way, sail a - way.
G        F            C              (G)
Sail a - way, sail a - way, sail a - way.
```

```
Verse 2
(C)        G                   F              C
From Bis - sau to Palau in the shade of Ava - lon.
          G                   F              C
From Fi - ji to Tiree and the isles of Ebo - ny
          G                    F               C
From Pe - ru to Cebu, feel the power of Baby - lon.
          G                    F               C
From Ba - li to Cali, far be - neath the Coral Sea.
```

```
Link 2
As Link 1
```

```
Bridge
C                       G                     Am F   G
Turn it up, turn it up, turn it up, up, adieu,   ooh.___
C                       G                     Am F   G
Turn it up, turn it up, turn it up, up, adieu,   ooh.___
Am7                     G                       F D
Turn it up, turn it up, turn it up, up, adieu,   oh.
```

```
Chorus 2
As Chorus 1
```

```
Verse 3
(C)      G                         F               C
From the North to the South, Ebu - dae unto Khar - toum.
         G                         F             C
From the deep Sea of Clouds to the Island of the Moon.
      G                      F               C
Carry me on the waves to the land I've never been.
      G                      F                C
Carry me on the waves to the lands I've never seen.
```

```
Verse 4
(C)    G                          F       C
We can sail, we can sail with the Orinoco flow.
       G                            F             C             (G)
We can sail, we can sail, (sail a - way, sail a - way, sail a - way).
(C)    G                           F              C
We can steer, we can near with Rob Dickins at the wheel.
       G                                F           C
We can sigh, say good-bye, Ross and his dependen - cies.
```

Verse 5

(C) G F C (G)
We can sail, we can sail, (sail a - way, sail a - way, sail a - way).
(C) G F C
We can reach, we can beach on the shores of Tripo - li.
G F C (G)
We can sail, we can sail, (sail a - way, sail a - way, sail a - way).
(C) G F C
From Ba - li to Cali, far be - neath the Coral Sea.
(C) G F C (G)
We can sail, we can sail, (sail a - way, sail a - way, sail a - way).
(C) G F C
From Bis - sau to Palau in the shade of Ava - lon.
(C) G F C (G)
We can sail, we can sail, (sail a - way, sail a - way, sail a - way).
(C)
We can reach, we can beach far be - yond the Yellow Sea.
(C) G F C (G)
We can sail, we can sail, (sail a - way, sail a - way, sail a - way).
(C) G F C
From Pe - ru to Cebu, feel the power of Baby - lon.
G F C (G)
We can sail, we can sail, (sail a - way, sail a - way, sail a - way).
(C) G F C (G)
We can sail, we can sail, (sail a - way, sail a - way, sail a - way).

Chorus 3

G F C G
Sail a - way, sail a - way, sail a - way.
G F C G
Sail a - way, sail a - way, sail a - way.
G F C G
Sail a - way, sail a - way, sail a - way.
G F C (G)
Sail a - way, sail a - way, sail a - way.

Outro

G F C
Ah.___
G F C
Ah.___
Cm
Ah.

Personal Jesus

Words & Music by Martin Gore

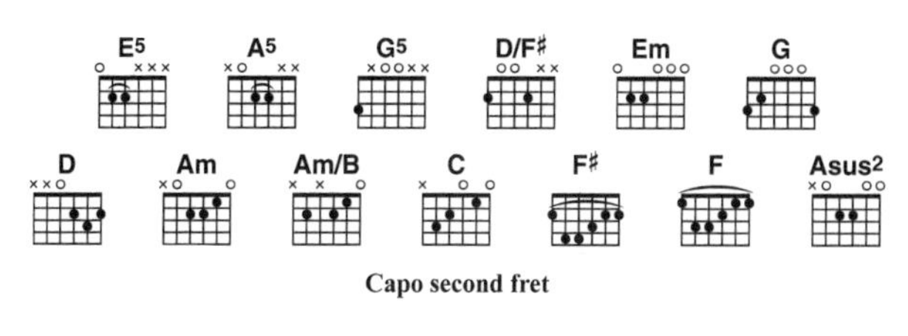

Capo second fret

```
            N.C.
Intro       Reach out and touch faith.

            |: E5   | E5   | E5   | E5   :|

            E5
Chorus 1    Your own personal Jesus,
                                                    A5    G5  D/F♯
            Someone to hear your prayers, someone who cares.
                E5
            Your own personal Jesus,
                                                     A5    G5  D/F♯
            Someone to hear your prayers, someone who's there.

Link 1      | E5   | E5   | E5   | E5   ||

            Em
Verse 1     Feeling's unknown and you're all alone,
            G                D
            Flesh and bone by the telephone,
            Am                 Am/B          C      Em
            Lift up the receiver, I'll make you a be - liever.
```

```
cont.        Take second best, put me to the test,
             G                          D
             Things on your chest, you need to confess,
             Am                 Am/B            C     Em
             I will deliver, you know I'm a for - giver.


             F♯ F                        Em
Pre-chorus      Reach out and touch faith.
             F♯ F                        Em
                Reach out and touch faith.


             E5
Chorus 2     Your own personal Jesus,
                                                        A5    G5 D/F♯
             Someone to hear your prayers, someone who cares.
                  E5
             Your own personal Jesus,
                                                          A5    G5 D/F♯
             Someone to hear your prayers, someone who's there.


Link 2       | F♯    | C     | N.C.  | N.C.  |

             | N.C.  | N.C.  | N.C.  | N.C.  |

             | E5    | E5    | E5    | E5    ||


             Em
Verse 2      Feelings unknown and you're all alone,
             G                       D
             Flesh and bone by the telephone,
             Am                           Am/B          C     Em
             Lift up the receiver, I'll make you a be - liever.
             Am                   Am/B
             I will deliver, you know I'm a for - giver.
```

```
          F♯ F
Outro        Reach out and touch faith.
               E5                   A5     G5
          Your own personal Jesus.
          F♯ F                              Em
             Reach out and touch faith.
          F♯ F                              Em
             Reach out and touch faith.
          F♯ F                              Em
             Reach out and touch faith.

          Reach, reach out,
          F♯ F                              Em
             Reach out and touch faith.
          F♯ F                              Asus2
             Reach out and touch faith.
```

Seven Nation Army

Words & Music by Jack White

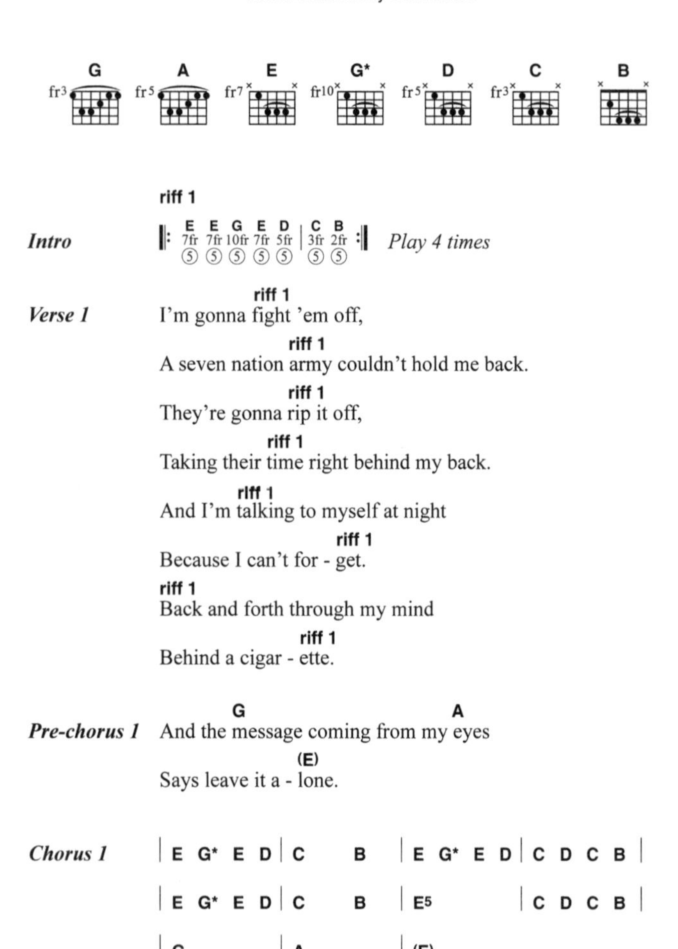

riff 1

Intro ‖: E 7fr ⑤ E 7fr ⑤ G 10fr ⑤ E 7fr ⑤ D 5fr ⑤ | C 3fr ⑤ B 2fr ⑤ :‖ *Play 4 times*

Verse 1

riff 1
I'm gonna fight 'em off,
riff 1
A seven nation army couldn't hold me back.
riff 1
They're gonna rip it off,
riff 1
Taking their time right behind my back.
riff 1
And I'm talking to myself at night
riff 1
Because I can't for - get.
riff 1
Back and forth through my mind
riff 1
Behind a cigar - ette.

Pre-chorus 1

G A
And the message coming from my eyes
(E)
Says leave it a - lone.

Chorus 1

| E G* E D | C B | E G* E D | C D C B |
| E G* E D | C B | E5 | C D C B |
| G | A | (E)

Link 1 𝄆 riff 1 𝄇 *Play 4 times*

Verse 2

```
             riff 1
Don't want to hear about it,
            riff 1
Every single one's got a story to tell.
         riff 1
Everyone knows about it,
                  riff 1
From the Queen of England to the hounds of hell.
        riff 1
And if I catch it coming back my way
                       riff 1
I'm gonna serve it to you.
    riff 1
And that ain't what you want to hear,
                   riff 1
But that's what I'll do.
```

Pre-chorus 2

```
        G                   A
And the feeling coming from my bones
           (E)
Says find a home.
```

Chorus 2
solo

Play 4 times

```
𝄆 E  G*  E  D | C     B   | E  G*  E  D | C  D  C  B 𝄇
| G           | A         | (E)
```

Link 2 𝄆 riff 1 𝄇 *Play 4 times*

Verse 3

```
                  riff 1
I'm going to Wichita,
                  riff 1
Far from this opera for evermore.
              riff 1
I'm gonna work the straw,
                    riff 1
Make the sweat drip out of every pore.
         riff 1
And I'm bleeding, and I'm bleeding, and I'm bleeding
                        riff 1
Right before the Lord.
        riff 1
All the words are gonna bleed from me
                          riff 1
And I will think no more.
```

Pre-chorus 3

```
           G                   A
And the screams coming from my blood
                 (E)
Tell me go back home.
```

Chorus 3

```
| E G* E D | C     B | E G* E D | C D C B |
| E G* E D | C     B | E G* E D | C D C B | E
```

Pretty In Pink

Words & Music by Richard Butler, John Ashton, Roger Morris,
Tim Butler, Duncan Kilburn & Vince Ely

Dsus4 D Gmaj7/B Dsus2/A Gsus4 G Asus4

A Cadd9 Cadd9♯11 C/E Em Em9 F♯(♭9)

Intro ‖: Dsus4 D | Dsus4 Gmaj7/B Dsus2/A | Gsus4 G | Asus4 A :‖

Verse 1

Dsus4 D Cadd9 Cadd9♯11
Caroline laughs and it's raining all day
C/E Em Asus4 A
She loves to be one of the girls
Dsus4 D Cadd9 Cadd9♯11
She lives in a place in the side of our lives
C/E Em Asus4 A
Where nothing is ever put straight
Dsus4 D Cadd9 Cadd9♯11
She turns herself around and she smiles and she says
C/E Em Asus4 A
"This is it that's the end of the joke."
Dsus4 D Cadd9 Cadd9♯11
And loses herself in her dreaming and sleep
C/E Em Asus4 A
And her lovers walk through in their coats, she's

Chorus 1

Em9 F♯(♭9) G
Pretty in pink
F♯(♭9) Em9
Isn't she___
F♯(♭9) G
Pretty in pink
F♯(♭9)
Isn't she.

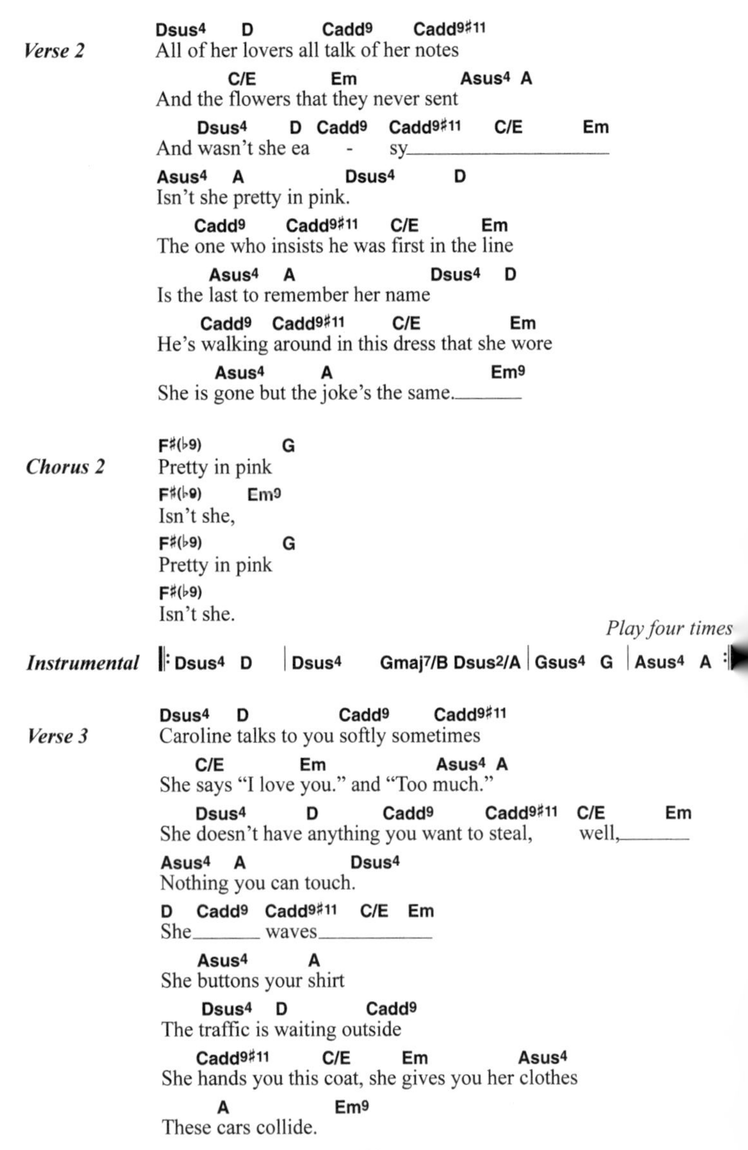

Verse 2

Dsus4 D Cadd9 Cadd9#11
All of her lovers all talk of her notes
C/E Em Asus4 A
And the flowers that they never sent
Dsus4 D Cadd9 Cadd9#11 C/E Em
And wasn't she ea - sy___________________
Asus4 A Dsus4 D
Isn't she pretty in pink.
Cadd9 Cadd9#11 C/E Em
The one who insists he was first in the line
Asus4 A Dsus4 D
Is the last to remember her name
Cadd9 Cadd9#11 C/E Em
He's walking around in this dress that she wore
Asus4 A Em9
She is gone but the joke's the same.______

Chorus 2

F#(b9) G
Pretty in pink
F#(b9) Em9
Isn't she,
F#(b9) G
Pretty in pink
F#(b9)
Isn't she.

Play four times

Instrumental ||: Dsus4 D | Dsus4 Gmaj7/B Dsus2/A | Gsus4 G | Asus4 A :||

Verse 3

Dsus4 D Cadd9 Cadd9#11
Caroline talks to you softly sometimes
C/E Em Asus4 A
She says "I love you." and "Too much."
Dsus4 D Cadd9 Cadd9#11 C/E Em
She doesn't have anything you want to steal, well,______
Asus4 A Dsus4
Nothing you can touch.
D Cadd9 Cadd9#11 C/E Em
She______ waves___________
Asus4 A
She buttons your shirt
Dsus4 D Cadd9
The traffic is waiting outside
Cadd9#11 C/E Em Asus4
She hands you this coat, she gives you her clothes
A Em9
These cars collide.

Chorus 3

F♯(♭9) G
Pretty in pink
F♯(♭9) Em9
Isn't she,
F♯(♭9) G
Pretty in pink
F♯(♭9)
Isn't she.

Play eight times

Outro ‖: Dsus4 D | Dsus4 Gmaj7/B Dsus2/A | Gsus4 G | Asus4 A :‖

| D ‖

A Rainy Night In Georgia

Words & Music by Tony Joe White

Dmaj7 (fr5) Cmaj7 (fr3) Gmaj7 Bm7 F♯m7 Em7 G Asus4

Intro | Dmaj7 | Cmaj7 | Dmaj7 | Cmaj7 ||

Verse 1

```
Dmaj7
Hovering by my suitcase,
Gmaj7                             Dmaj7
Trying to find a warm place to spend the night.

Heavy rain falling,
Gmaj7                                 Dmaj7
Seems I hear your voice calling "It's all right."
```

Chorus 1

```
Bm7                  F♯m7
   A rainy night in Georgia,
Bm7                  F♯m7
   A rainy night in Georgia,
  Em7                     G              Dmaj7
It seems like it's raining all over the world,
  Cmaj7                             Dmaj7
I feel like it's raining all over the world.
```

Verse 2

```
Dmaj7
Neon signs a-flashing,
Gmaj7                            Dmaj7
Taxi cabs and buses passing through the night.

A distant moaning of a train
Gmaj7                          Dmaj7
Seems to play a sad refrain      to the night.
```

Chorus 2

```
Bm7                  F♯m7
   A rainy night in Georgia,
Bm7                     F♯m7
   Such a rainy night      in Georgia,
```

cont.

```
Em7                   G                    Dmaj7
   Lord, I believe it's raining all over the world,
Cmaj7                               Dmaj7
   I feel like it's raining all over the world.
```

Bridge

```
Cmaj7                 Dmaj7
   How many times I wondered,
Cmaj7           Dmaj7
   It still comes out the same.
Gmaj7   F#m7                  Em7
No matter   how you look at it   or think of it,
    Gmaj7 F#m7    Em7      Asus4
It's life    and you just got to play the game.
```

Instrumental | Dmaj7 | Cmaj7 | Dmaj7 | Cmaj7 ||

Verse 3

```
 Dmaj7
I find me a place in a box car,
    Gmaj7           Dmaj7
So I take my guitar to pass some time.

Late at night when it's hard to rest,
 Gmaj7                            Dmaj7
I hold your picture to my chest and I feel fine.
```

Chorus 3

```
Bm7                         F#m7
   But it's a rainy night in Georgia,
Bm7                           F#m7
   Baby, it's a rainy night in    Georgia,
Em7  G                    Dmaj7
     I feel it's raining all over the world,
      Em7                 G                    Dmaj7
Kinda lonely now, and it's raining all over the world.
   Em7                          G
Oh,___ have you ever been lonely, people?
         Dmaj7                                   Em7
And you feel that it was raining all over this man's world.
       G                               Dmaj7
You're talking about a-raining, raining, raining, raining,

Raining, raining, raining, raining, raining, raining,
Em7                     G                     Dmaj7  Bm7
Raining, a-raining, a - raining, raining over the world.
```

Em7 G Dmaj7 *Ad lib. to fade*

Reach Out I'll Be There

Words & Music by Brian Holland, Eddie Holland & Lamont Dozier

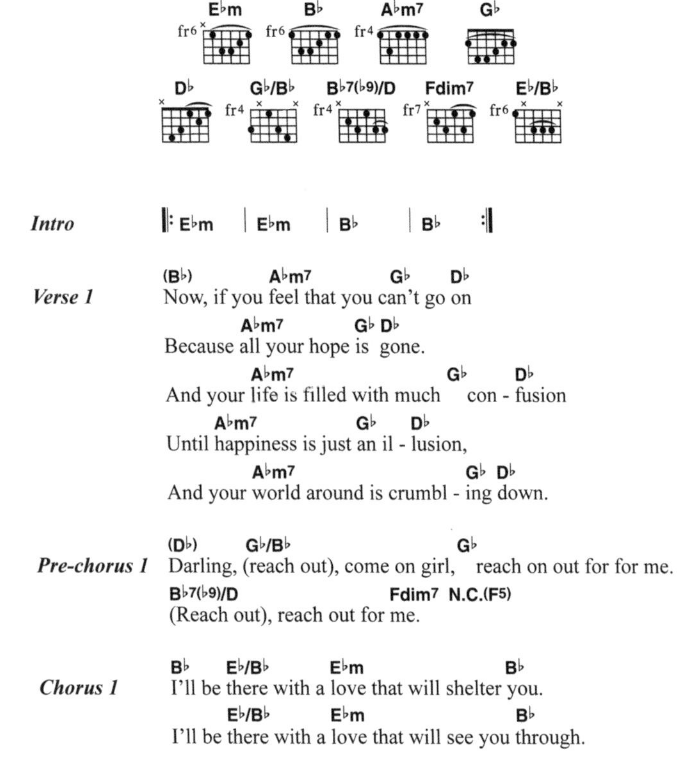

Intro ‖: E♭m | E♭m | B♭ | B♭ :‖

Verse 1

(B♭) A♭m7 G♭ D♭
Now, if you feel that you can't go on

A♭m7 G♭ D♭
Because all your hope is gone.

A♭m7 G♭ D♭
And your life is filled with much con - fusion

A♭m7 G♭ D♭
Until happiness is just an il - lusion,

A♭m7 G♭ D♭
And your world around is crumbl - ing down.

Pre-chorus 1

(D♭) G♭/B♭ G♭
Darling, (reach out), come on girl, reach on out for for me.

B♭7(♭9)/D Fdim7 N.C.(F5)
(Reach out), reach out for me.

Chorus 1

B♭ E♭/B♭ E♭m B♭
I'll be there with a love that will shelter you.

E♭/B♭ E♭m B♭
I'll be there with a love that will see you through.

Verse 2

```
B♭              A♭m7          G♭      D♭
When you're lost and about to give up
                A♭m7          G♭      D♭
'Cause your best just ain't good e - nough.
            A♭m7              G♭      D♭
And you feel the world has grown cold
              A♭m7            G♭      D♭
And you're drifting out all on your own,
            A♭m7   G♭    D♭
And you need a hand to hold.
```

Pre-chorus 2 As Pre-chorus 1

Chorus 2

```
B♭      E♭/B♭   E♭m                 B♭
I'll be there to love and comfort you.
                E♭/B♭  E♭m                     B♭
And I'll be there to cherish and care for you.
```

Bridge

```
B♭      E♭/B♭   E♭m              B♭
I'll be there to always see you through.
        E♭/B♭   E♭m                B♭
I'll be there to love and comfort you.
```

Verse 3

```
B♭   A♭m7                  G♭      D♭
I can tell the way I hang    your head,
                   A♭m7      G♭            D♭
You're without love now, now you're afraid.
                      A♭m7           G♭  D♭
And through your tears you look a - round,
               A♭m7              G♭    D♭
But there's no peace of mind to be found.

I know what you're thinking,
A♭m7                  G♭  D♭
   You're alone now,      no love of your own.
```

Pre-chorus 3

```
(D♭)           G♭/B♭                       G♭
But darling, (reach out), come on girl,     reach on out for for me.
B♭7(♭9)/D   Fdim7  N.C.(F5)
Reach out.                   Just look over your shoulder.
```

Chorus 3

```
B♭     E♭/B♭   E♭m                          B♭
I'll be there to give you all the love you need.
                 E♭/B♭          E♭m              B♭
And I'll be there, you can always depend on me.     To fade
```

Rio

Words & Music by Duran Duran

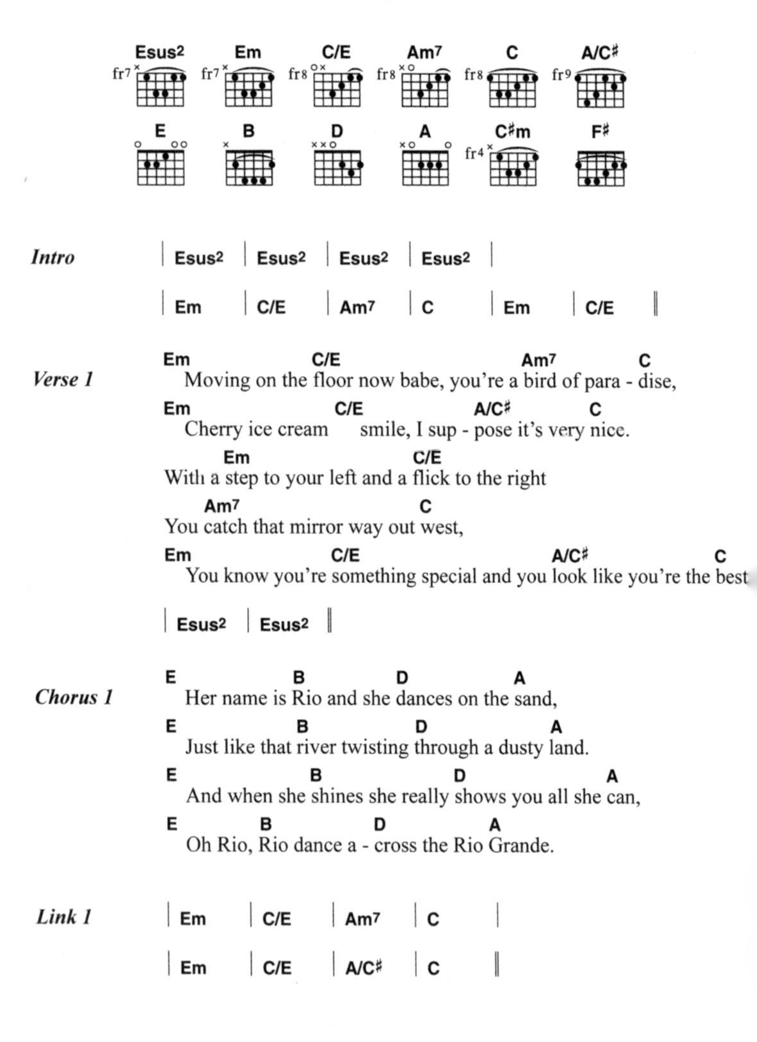

Intro | Esus2 | Esus2 | Esus2 | Esus2 |

| Em | C/E | Am7 | C | Em | C/E ||

Verse 1

Em C/E Am7 C
Moving on the floor now babe, you're a bird of para - dise,
Em C/E A/C♯ C
Cherry ice cream smile, I sup - pose it's very nice.
Em C/E
With a step to your left and a flick to the right
Am7 C
You catch that mirror way out west,
Em C/E A/C♯ C
You know you're something special and you look like you're the best

| Esus2 | Esus2 ||

Chorus 1

E B D A
Her name is Rio and she dances on the sand,
E B D A
Just like that river twisting through a dusty land.
E B D A
And when she shines she really shows you all she can,
E B D A
Oh Rio, Rio dance a - cross the Rio Grande.

Link 1 | Em | C/E | Am7 | C |

| Em | C/E | A/C♯ | C ||

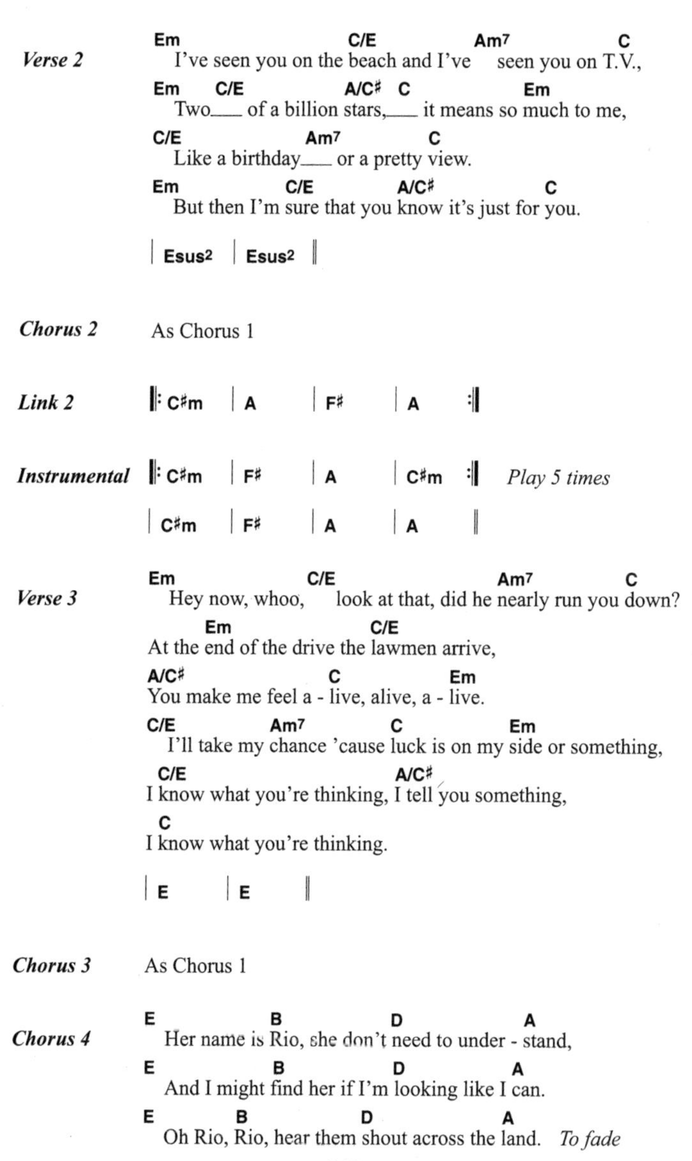

Verse 2

Em C/E Am7 C
I've seen you on the beach and I've seen you on T.V.,
Em C/E A/C♯ C Em
Two___ of a billion stars,___ it means so much to me,
C/E Am7 C
Like a birthday___ or a pretty view.
Em C/E A/C♯ C
But then I'm sure that you know it's just for you.

| Esus2 | Esus2 ||

Chorus 2

As Chorus 1

Link 2

|: C♯m | A | F♯ | A :|

Instrumental

|: C♯m | F♯ | A | C♯m :| *Play 5 times*

| C♯m | F♯ | A | A ||

Verse 3

Em C/E Am7 C
Hey now, whoo, look at that, did he nearly run you down?
Em C/E
At the end of the drive the lawmen arrive,
A/C♯ C Em
You make me feel a - live, alive, a - live.
C/E Am7 C Em
I'll take my chance 'cause luck is on my side or something,
C/E A/C♯
I know what you're thinking, I tell you something,
C
I know what you're thinking.

| E | E ||

Chorus 3

As Chorus 1

Chorus 4

E B D A
Her name is Rio, she don't need to under - stand,
E B D A
And I might find her if I'm looking like I can.
E B D A
Oh Rio, Rio, hear them shout across the land. *To fade*

Sledgehammer

Words & Music by Peter Gabriel

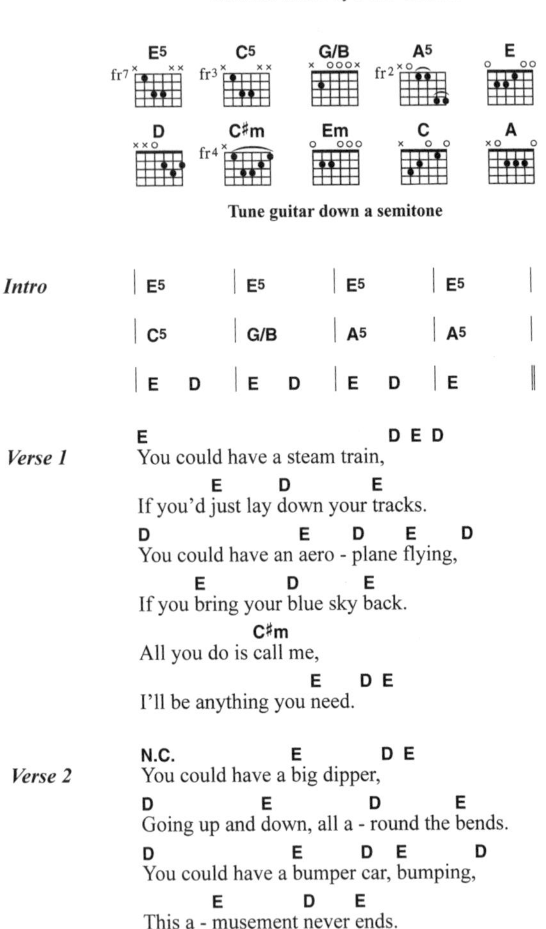

Tune guitar down a semitone

Intro

```
| E5      | E5      | E5      | E5      |
| C5      | G/B     | A5      | A5      |
| E   D   | E   D   | E   D   | E       ||
```

Verse 1

```
E                              D E D
You could have a steam train,
           E     D        E
If you'd just lay down your tracks.
D                    E      D     E       D
You could have an aero - plane flying,
        E           D     E
If you bring your blue sky back.
               C♯m
All you do is call me,
                          E    D E
I'll be anything you need.
```

Verse 2

```
N.C.                    E         D E
You could have a big dipper,
D                E                 D           E
Going up and down, all a - round the bends.
D                       E       D  E         D
You could have a bumper car, bumping,
           E          D     E
This a - musement never ends.
```

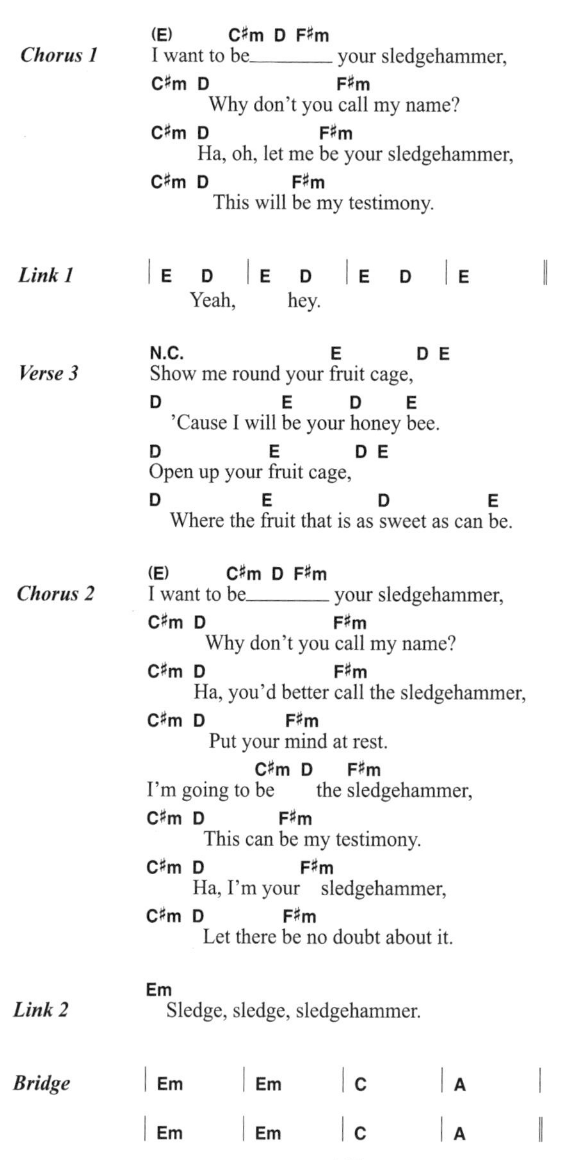

Chorus 1

(E) C♯m D F♯m
I want to be________ your sledgehammer,
C♯m D F♯m
Why don't you call my name?
C♯m D F♯m
Ha, oh, let me be your sledgehammer,
C♯m D F♯m
This will be my testimony.

Link 1

| E D | E D | E D | E ‖
Yeah, hey.

Verse 3

N.C. E D E
Show me round your fruit cage,
D E D E
'Cause I will be your honey bee.
D E D E
Open up your fruit cage,
D E D E
Where the fruit that is as sweet as can be.

Chorus 2

(E) C♯m D F♯m
I want to be________ your sledgehammer,
C♯m D F♯m
Why don't you call my name?
C♯m D F♯m
Ha, you'd better call the sledgehammer,
C♯m D F♯m
Put your mind at rest.
C♯m D F♯m
I'm going to be the sledgehammer,
C♯m D F♯m
This can be my testimony.
C♯m D F♯m
Ha, I'm your sledgehammer,
C♯m D F♯m
Let there be no doubt about it.

Link 2

Em
Sledge, sledge, sledgehammer.

Bridge

| Em | Em | C | A |
| Em | Em | C | A ‖

Outro

```
(A)
Oh, get a ring.
Em
   I kicked the habit, (kicked the habit, kicked the habit)
C                 A
   Shed my skin.    (shed my skin)
Em
   This is the new stuff, (this is the new stuff)
    C                      A
I go   dancing in. (we go dancing in)
                    Em
Oh, won't you show for me, (show for me)
      C                A
I will   show for you.    (show for you)
        Em
Please    show for me, (show for me)
      C
I will   show for you.
A                                            Em
Yeah, yeah, yeah, yeah, yeah, I do mean you.

(Show for me), only you,
                          C
You've been coming through,
                          A
I'm gonna build that power,
                         Em
Build, build up that power, hey.

I've been feeding the rhythm, huh,
                           C
I've been feeding the rhythm.
                   A                 Em
Gonna feel that power, hey, build in you.

Ha, come on, come on, help me do,
                         C
Come on, come on, help me do,
A                                                  Em
Yeah, yeah, yeah, yeah, yeah, yeah, yeah, yeah, you.

I've been feeding the rhythm,
                           C
I've been feeding the rhythm,
```

cont.

Em
It's what we're doing, doing all day and night.

Come on, come on, help me do,

C
Come on, come on, help me do,

A Em
Yeah, yeah, yeah, yeah, yeah, yeah, yeah, yeah, you. *To fade*

Smoke On The Water

Words & Music by Ian Gillan, Ritchie Blackmore, Jon Lord, Roger Glover & Ian Paice

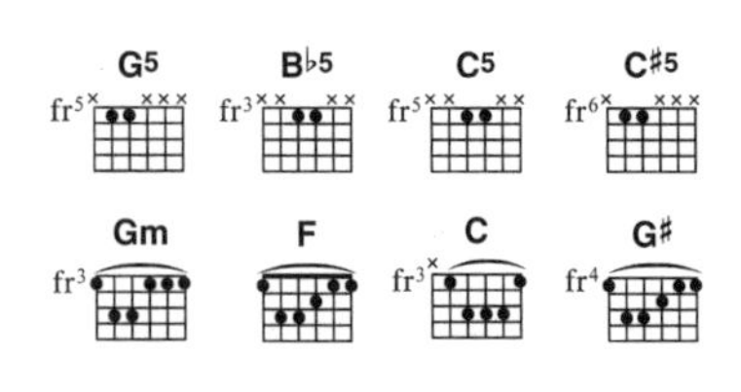

Play 8 times

Intro ‖: G5 B♭5 C G5 | B♭5 C♯5 C5 | G5 B♭5 C5 B♭5 | G5 :‖

Verse 1

```
   Gm                                                F    Gm
We all came down to Montreux, on the Lake Geneva shoreline
                              F      Gm
To make records with a mobile,  we didn't have much time.
                                             F            Gm
Frank Zappa and the Mothers were at the best place around
                                              F        Gm
But some stupid with a flare gun, burned the place to the ground.
```

Chorus 1

```
C                G♯     Gm
Smoke, on the water,    fire in the sky.
C                G♯
Smoke, on the water.
```

Link ‖: G5 B♭5 C G5 | B♭5 C♯5 C5 | G5 B♭5 C5 B♭5 | G5 :‖

Verse 2

```
Gm                                                       F      Gm
   They burned down the gambling house, it died with an awful sound
                                F              Gm
Funky Claude was running in and out,   pulling kids out the ground.
                                      F       Gm
When it was all over, we had to find another place,
                                                  F          Gm
Swiss time was running out, it seemed that we would lose the race.
```

Chorus 2 As Chorus 1

Instrumental ||: G5 B♭5 C G5 | B♭5 C♯5 C5 | G5 B♭5 C5 B♭5 | G5 :||

||: Gm | Gm | C | Gm | Gm | Gm | C | Gm :||

| C | C | F | F |

||: G5 B♭5 C G5 | B♭5 C♯5 C5 | G5 B♭5 C5 B♭5 | G5 :||

Verse 3

```
Gm                                                        F        Gm
   We ended up at the Grand Hotel, it was empty, cold and bare.

But with the Rolling truck Stones thing just outside,
F                  Gm
  Making our music there with a few red lights, a few old beds,
                  F          Gm
We made a place to sweat,
                                                          F                     Gm
No matter what we get out of this, I know,   I know we'll never forget.
```

Chorus 3

```
C                    G♯       Gm
Smoke, on the water, fire in the sky.
C                    G♯
Smoke, on the water.
```

Outro ||: G5 B♭5 C G5 | B♭5 C♯5 C5 | G5 B♭5 C5 B♭5 | G5 :||

Repeat to fade

Song 2

Music by Damon Albarn, Graham Coxon, Alex James & David Rowntree

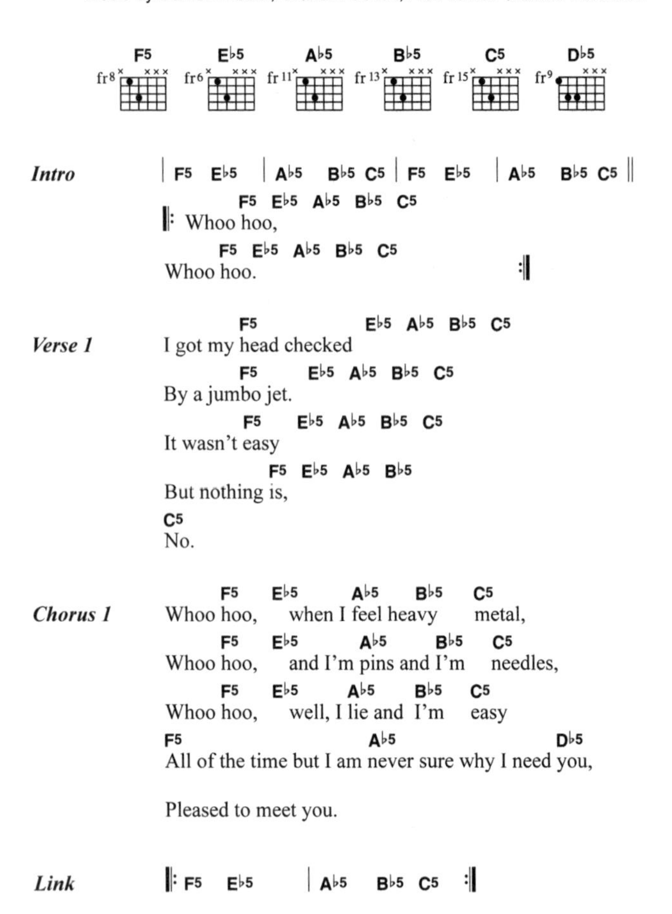

Intro

| F5 E♭5 | A♭5 B♭5 C5 | F5 E♭5 | A♭5 B♭5 C5 ||

F5 E♭5 A♭5 B♭5 C5
||: Whoo hoo,

F5 E♭5 A♭5 B♭5 C5
Whoo hoo. :||

Verse 1

F5 E♭5 A♭5 B♭5 C5
I got my head checked

F5 E♭5 A♭5 B♭5 C5
By a jumbo jet.

F5 E♭5 A♭5 B♭5 C5
It wasn't easy

F5 E♭5 A♭5 B♭5
But nothing is,

C5
No.

Chorus 1

F5 E♭5 A♭5 B♭5 C5
Whoo hoo, when I feel heavy metal,

F5 E♭5 A♭5 B♭5 C5
Whoo hoo, and I'm pins and I'm needles,

F5 E♭5 A♭5 B♭5 C5
Whoo hoo, well, I lie and I'm easy

F5 A♭5 D♭5
All of the time but I am never sure why I need you,

Pleased to meet you.

Link

||: F5 E♭5 | A♭5 B♭5 C5 :||

```
                   F5              E♭5  A♭5  B♭5  C5
Verse 2     I got my head done
                      F5       E♭5  A♭5  B♭5  C5
            When I was young,
                     F5        E♭5  A♭5  B♭5  C5
            It's not my problem,
                       F5      E♭5  A♭5  B♭5  C5
            It's not my problem.

                  F5     E♭5      A♭5     B♭5     C5
Chorus 2    Whoo hoo,    when I feel heavy     metal,
                  F5     E♭5       A♭5      B♭5    C5
            Whoo hoo,    and I'm pins and I'm    needles,
                  F5     E♭5      A♭5     B♭5    C5
            Whoo hoo,    well, I lie and  I'm    easy
            F5                          A♭5                  D♭5
            All of the time but I am never sure why I need you,

            Pleased to meet you.

Outro       | F5    E♭5   | A♭5    B♭5   C5   | F5    E♭5   |
                                        Yeah,  yeah.

            | A♭5    B♭5   C5   | F5    E♭5   | A♭5    B♭5   C5   |
                             Yeah,  yeah.                     Yeah,

            | F5    E♭5   | A♭5    B♭5   C5   | F5          ||
              yeah.                      Oh,    yeah.
```

Stupid Cupid

Words & Music by Howard Greenfield & Neil Sedaka

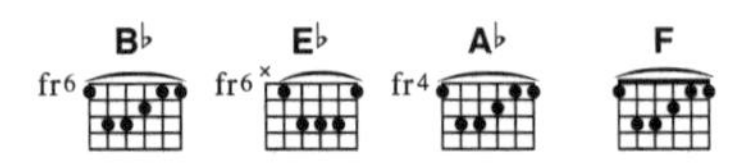

Intro | B♭ ‖

Verse 1

E♭ N.C. E♭
Stupid Cupid, you're a real mean guy, (Stupid Cupid)
A♭
I'd like to clip your wings so you can't fly. (Stupid Cupid)
E♭
I'm in love and it's a crying shame, (Stupid Cupid)
B♭
And I know that you're the one to blame. (Stupid Cupid)
A♭
Hey, hey, set me free,
E♭ N.C.
Stupid Cupid, stop pickin' on me.

Verse 2

E♭
I can't do my homework and I can't see straight, (Stupid Cupid)
A♭
I meet him every morning 'bout a-half-past eight. (Stupid Cupid)
E♭
I'm acting like a lovesick fool, (Stupid Cupid)
B♭
You've even got me carrying his books to school. (Stupid Cupid)
A♭
Hey, hey, set me free,
E♭ N.C.
Stupid Cupid, stop pickin' on me.

```
              A♭                                    E♭
*Bridge*        You fixed me up but good right from the very start,
              A♭                                 F              B♭
              Hey, go play Robin Hood with somebody else's heart.

              E♭
*Verse 3*       You've got me jumping like a crazy clown, (Stupid Cupid)
                                                                  A♭
              And I don't feature what you're putting down. (Stupid Cupid)
                                                        E♭
              Since I kissed his loving lips of wine, (Stupid Cupid)
                                                                 B♭
              The thing that bothers me is that I like it fine. (Stupid Cupid)
                          A♭
              Hey, hey, set me free,
              E♭  N.C.
                 Stupid Cupid, stop pickin' on me.

*Instrumental* | A♭      | A♭      | E♭      | E♭      |

              | A♭      | A♭      | F       | B♭      ||

              E♭  N.C.                                            E♭
*Verse 4*          You've got me jumping like a crazy clown, (Stupid Cupid)
                                                                  A♭
              And I don't feature what you're putting down. (Stupid Cupid)
                                                        E♭
              Since I kissed his loving lips of wine, (Stupid Cupid)
                                                                 B♭
              The thing that bothers me is that I like it fine. (Stupid Cupid)
                          A♭
              Hey, hey, set me free.
              E♭  N.C.
                  Stupid Cupid, stop pickin' on me.
              B♭          A♭
                 Hey, hey, set me free
              E♭  N.C.
                  Stupid Cupid, stop pickin' on me.

              N.C.    E♭
*Outro*         (Stupid Cupid, Stupid Cupid, Stupid Cupid, Stupid Cupid.)   *To fade*
```

Start Me Up

Words & Music by Mick Jagger & Keith Richards

C fr5 | F(add9)/C fr5 | B♭ | E♭(add9)/B♭ fr3 | F fr10 | E♭ fr8 | D fr7 | E fr9

⑥ = D ③ = G
⑤ = G ② = B
④ = D ① = D

Intro

‖: C F(add9)/C | C F(add9)/C |
| B♭ E♭(add9)/B♭ B♭ E♭(add9)/B♭ | B♭ E♭(add9)/B♭ B♭ E♭(add9)/B♭ :‖

Verse 1

```
B♭      C           F(add9)/C
If you start me up,
C   F(add9)/C C             F(add9)/C  B♭
    If        you start me up I'll never stop.
        C           F(add9)/C
If you start me up,
C   F(add9)/C C             F(add9)/C  B♭
    If        you start me up I'll never stop.
```

Verse 2

```
B♭           C          F(add9)/C
I've been running hot,
C   F(add9)/C   C           F(add9)/C  B♭
    You got me, reckon I don't       blow my top.
        C           F(add9)/C
If you start me up,
C   F(add9)/C C             F(add9)/C  B♭
    If        you start me up I'll never stop,
```

Never stop, never stop, never stop.

Chorus 1

C F E♭ D
You make a grown man cry.

C F E♭ D
You make a grown man cry.

C F E♭ D
You make a grown man cry.

C F(add9)/C C F(add9)/C C
Spread out the oil, the gas - o - line,

D E♭ F(add9)/C
I walk smooth, ride in a mean, mean ma - chine,

C F(add9)/C C F(add9)/C B♭
Start it up.

Verse 3

B♭ C F(add9)/C
If you start me up,

C F(add9)/C C F(add9)/C B♭
Kick on the starter give it all you got, you got, you got.

C F(add9)/C
I can't com - pete

C F(add9)/C C F(add9)/C B♭
With the riders in the other heats.

C F(add9)/C
If you rough it up,

C F(add9)/C C F(add9)/C B♭
If you like it you can slide it up,

Slide it up, slide it up, slide it up.

Chorus 2

C F E♭ D
Don't make a grown man cry.

C F E♭ D
Don't make a grown man cry.

C F E♭ D
Don't make a grown man cry.

C F(add9)/C C F(add9)/C C
My eyes di - late, my lips go green,

D E♭ F(add9)/C
My hands are greasy, she's a mean, mean ma - chine,

C F(add9)/C C F(add9)/C B♭
Start it up.

Verse 4

C F(add9)/C
Start me up,
C F(add9)/C C F(add9)/C B♭
Ah,__ give it all you got,

You got to never, never, never stop.
C F(add9)/C
Slide it up,
C F(add9)/C C F(add9)/C B♭
Oh, baby just a - slide it up

Slide it up, slide it up, never, never, never.

Chorus 3

C F E♭ D
You make a grown man cry.
C F E♭ D
You make a grown man cry.
C F E♭ D
You make a grown man cry.
C F(add9)/C C F(add9)/C C
Ride like the wind at double speed,
D E♭ F(add9)/C
I'll take you places that you've never, never seen.
C F(add9)/C C F(add9)/C B♭

Verse 5

C F(add9)/C
Start it up.
C F(add9)/C C F(add9)/C B♭
Love the day when we'll never stop, never stop

Never, never, never stop.
C F(add9)/C
Tough me up,
C F(add9)/C C F(add9)/C B♭
Never stop, never stop.

Outro

C F(add9)/C C F(add9)/C C F(add9)/C B♭
You, you, you make a grown man cry.
C F(add9)/C C F(add9)/C C F(add9)/C B♭
You, you make a dead man come.
C F(add9)/C C F(add9)/C C F(add9)/C B♭
You, you make a dead man come.

Repeat ad lib. to fa

Take Your Mama

Words & Music by Jason Sellards & Scott Hoffman

B♭ fr6 | B♭7sus4 fr6 | B♭7 fr6 | A♭ fr4 | A♭7sus4 fr4 | A♭7 fr4

Cm fr3 | Csus2 fr3 | Cm7/B♭ fr3 | Am7♭5 fr4 | Fm | A fr5

Intro

```
|: B♭       | B♭  B♭7sus4  B♭7 | A♭       | A♭  A♭7sus4  A♭7 |
|  Cm       | Cm  Csus2  Cm    | B♭       | B♭  B♭7sus4  B♭7 :|
```

Verse 1

```
(B♭7)   B♭                                     A♭
When you grow up living like a good boy oughta
               Cm                           B♭
And your mama takes a shine to her best son.
                                              A♭
Something different, all the girls they seem to like you
                     Cm                                     B♭
'Cause you're handsome, like to talk and a whole lot of fun.
```

Bridge 1

```
(B♭)               Cm                Cm7/B♭
But now your girl has gone a - missing
                Am7♭5            Fm     B♭
And your house has got an empty bed.
                  Cm                 Cm7/B♭
The folks'll wonder 'bout the wedding,
                  Am7♭5      Fm         B♭
They won't listen to a word you said.
```

```
                 B♭
Pre-chorus 1     We're gonna take your mama out all night,
                           A♭
                 Yeah, we'll show her what it's all about.
                            E♭
                 We'll get her jacked up on some cheap champagne,
                            B♭
                 We'll let the good times all roll out.

                 And if the music ain't good, well it's just too bad,
                            A♭
                 We're gonna sing along no matter what.
                           E♭
                 Because the dancers don't mind at the New Orleans,
                      B♭                          A♭  A
                 If you tip 'em and they make a cut.

                 B♭
Chorus 1         Do it, take your mama out all night,
                        E♭                                         B♭
                 So she'll have no doubt that we're doing all the best we can.
                 A♭       A     B♭                     A♭
                   We're gonna do it, take your mama out all night,
                         E♭                                      B♭   A♭  A
                 You can stay up late 'cause baby you're a full grown man.


Link 1           | B♭      | B♭  B♭7sus4  B♭7 | A♭      | A♭  A♭7sus4  A♭7 |

                 | Cm      | Cm  Csus2  Cm    | B♭      | B♭  B♭7sus4  B♭7 ||

                 (B♭7) B♭                              A♭
Verse 2          It's a struggle living like a good boy oughta,
                      Cm                                B♭
                 In the summer watching all the girls pass by.
                                                                A♭
                 When your mama heard the way that you'd been talking,
                        Cm                                B♭
                 I tried to tell you that all she'd wanna do is cry.
```

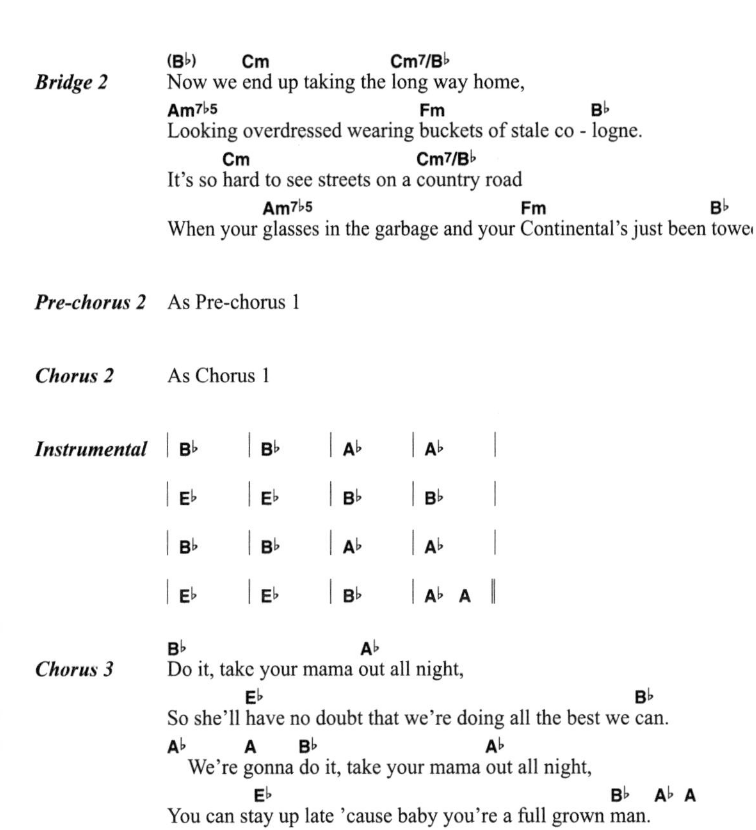

Bridge 2

(B♭) Cm Cm7/B♭
Now we end up taking the long way home,
Am7♭5 Fm B♭
Looking overdressed wearing buckets of stale co - logne.
Cm Cm7/B♭
It's so hard to see streets on a country road
Am7♭5 Fm B♭
When your glasses in the garbage and your Continental's just been towe

Pre-chorus 2 As Pre-chorus 1

Chorus 2 As Chorus 1

Instrumental

B♭	B♭	A♭	A♭
E♭	E♭	B♭	B♭
B♭	B♭	A♭	A♭
E♭	E♭	B♭	A♭ A	

Chorus 3

B♭ A♭
Do it, take your mama out all night,
E♭ B♭
So she'll have no doubt that we're doing all the best we can.
A♭ A B♭ A♭
We're gonna do it, take your mama out all night,
E♭ B♭ A♭ A
You can stay up late 'cause baby you're a full grown man.

The Tears Of A Clown

Words & Music by William "Smokey" Robinson, Stevie Wonder & Henry Cosby

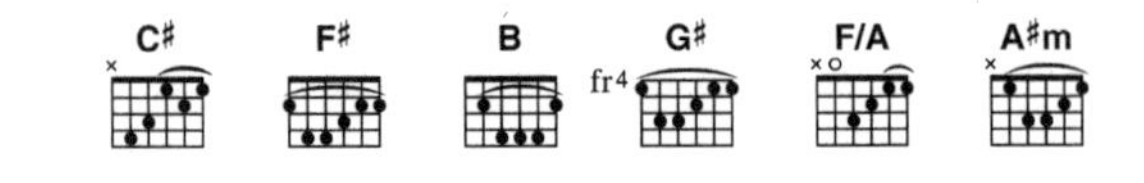

Intro | N.C.(C#) | N.C.(C#) | N.C.(C#) | N.C.(C#) |

C# F# B F#   C#   F# B F#
Oh, yeah, yeah, yeah.

Verse 1

(F#)   C#   F#   B
Now if there's a smile on my face,
F#   C#   F#   B
It's only there trying to fool the public,
F#   C#   F#   B
But when it comes down to fooling you;
F#   C#   F#   B
Now honey, that's quite a different subject.
F#   C#   F#   B
But don't let my glad ex - pression
F#   C#   F#   B
Give you the wrong im - pression.
F#   C#   F# B   F#   C#   F#
Really I'm sad,   oh, sadder than sad.
B   F#   C# F#
You're gone and I'm hurting so bad.
B   F#   C#   F# B F#
Like a clown I pre - tend to be glad.

```
            (F♯)                G♯                       F/A
Chorus 1    Now there's some sad things known to man,
                     A♯m                F♯
            But ain't too much sadder than
                          N.C.(C♯)
            The tears of a clown

            When there's no one around.

            C♯  F♯  B  F♯      C♯  F♯  B  F♯
Link 1                 Oh yeah, baby.

            (F♯)           C♯      F♯        B
Verse 2     Now if I ap - pear to be care - free,
                F♯        C♯         F♯         B
            It's only to camou - flage my sadness.
              F♯        C♯           F♯      B
            In order to shield my pride I try
               F♯         C♯             F♯        B
            To cover the hurt with a show of gladness.
            F♯              C♯      F♯          B
               But don't let my show con - vince you
            F♯        C♯          F♯     B
               That I've been happy since you
                 F♯         C♯  F♯ B    F♯          C♯  F♯
            De - cided to go,       oh, I need you so.
                B            F♯           C♯     F♯
            I'm hurt and I want you to know,
                   B          F♯        C♯     F♯
            But for others I put on a show.

            B   F♯                  G♯                       F/A
Chorus 2    Ooh well, there's some sad things known to man,
                     A♯m                F♯
            But ain't too much sadder than
                          N.C.(C♯)
            The tears of a clown

            When there's no one around. Oh yeah.
```

```
              C♯      F♯            B    F♯
Verse 3         Just like Pagli - acci did,
              C♯         F♯        B        F♯
                I try to keep my sadness hid.
              C♯             F♯      B   F♯
              Smilin' in the public eye
                            C♯      F♯      B
              While in my lonely room I cry
                  F♯         N.C.(C♯)
              The tears of a clown
                                          (C♯)
              When there's no one a - round.

              C♯  F♯  B  F♯
Link 2                   Oh yeah, baby.

              (F♯)                C♯     F♯     B     F♯
Outro         Now if there's a smile on my face,
                    C♯     F♯         B          F♯
              Don't let my glad ex - pression
                   C♯      F♯             B        F♯
              Give you the wrong im - pression.
                    C♯     F♯      B      F♯
              Don't let this smile I wear
                        C♯                F♯     B
              To make you think that I don't care.
              F♯                C♯  F♯  B  F♯
              Really I'm sad.                   To fade
```

Total Eclipse Of The Heart

Words & Music by Jim Steinman

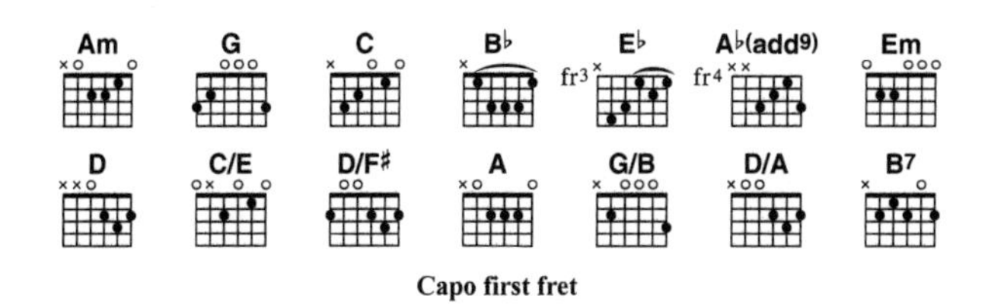

Capo first fret

Intro | Am | Am ||

Verse 1

Am
Turn around,

                                        G
Every now and then I get a little bit lonely

And you're never coming round.

Am
Turn around,

                                        G
Every now and then I get a little bit tired

                                        C
Of listening to the sound of my tears.

Turn around,

                                        B♭
Every now and then I get a little bit nervous

                                        C
That the best of all the years have gone by.

Turn around,

                                        B♭
Every now and then I get a little bit terrified

And then I see the look in your eyes.

```
             E♭            A♭(add9)
Bridge 1     Turn around bright eyes,

             Every now and then I fall apart.
             E♭            A♭(add9)
             Turn around bright eyes,
                                          (G)
             Every now and then I fall a - part.

             G      Em             C
Pre-chorus 1   And I need you now to - night,
                 D                  G
             And I need you more than ever.
                       Em           C
             And if you only hold me tight,
                    D              G
             We'll be holding on for - ever.
                      Em                C
             And we'll only be making it right,
                        D
             'Cause we'll never be wrong.
                C/E                          D/F♯
             To - gether we can take it to the end of the line,
                  C/E                          A
             Your love is like a shadow on me all of the time.
               G                               D/F♯
             I don't know what to do and I'm always in the dark,
                  Em                               A
             We're living in a powder keg and giving off sparks.
                                 G/B
             I really need you to - night,
                  D/A            G/B     C
             For - ever's gonna to start to - night,
                  D                      (G)
             For - ever's gonna to start to - night.
```

Chorus 1

```
G                      Em
Once upon a time I was falling in love,
    B7                       C
But now I'm only falling a - part.
G/B        Am
   There's nothing I can do,
  D                    G     Em C D
A total eclipse of the heart.
G                          Em
Once upon a time there was light in my life,
    B7                           C
But now there's only love in the dark.
G/B   Am
      Nothing I can say,
  D                    (G)
A total eclipse of the heart.
```

Link

```
| G     | Em    | C     | D     | C     | G     ||
```

Instrumental

```
| Am    | Am    | G     | G     | Am    | Am    |
| G     | G     | C     | C     | B♭    | B♭    |
| C     | C     | B♭    | B♭    ||
```

Bridge 2 As Bridge 1

Pre-chorus 2 As Pre-chorus 1

Chorus 2

```
G                      Em
Once upon a time I was falling in love,
    B7                       C
But now I'm only falling a - part.
G/B        Am
   There's nothing I can say,
  D                    G     Em C
A total eclipse of the heart.
  D                    G     Em C
A total eclipse of the heart.
  D                    G     Em C D
A total eclipse of the heart.
            G          Em C D
Turn around bright eyes.          To fade
```

Toxic

Words & Music by Cathy Dennis, Christian Karlsson, Pontus Winnberg & Henrik Jonback

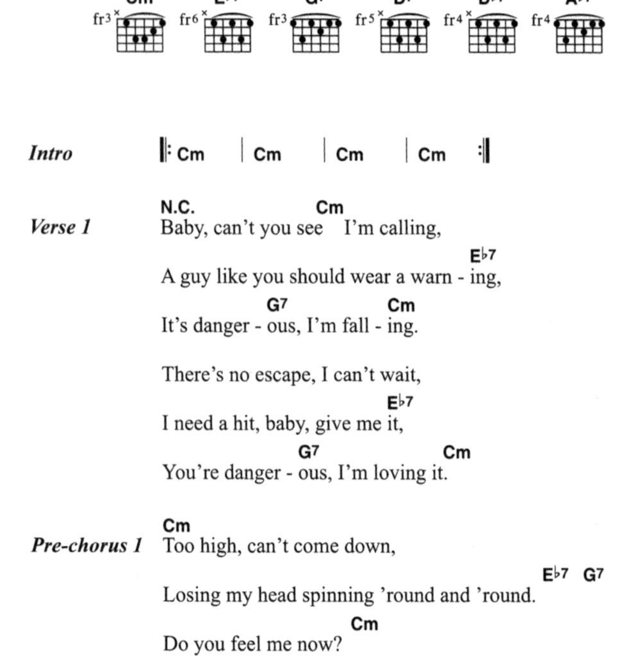

Chorus 1

Cm E♭7
With a taste of your lips I'm on a ride,
D7 D♭7
You're toxic, I'm slipping under.
Cm E♭7
With a taste of a poison paradise,
A♭7
I'm addicted to you,
G7 D♭7 Cm
Don't you know that you're toxic?
E♭7 D7
And I love what you do,
D♭7 Cm E♭7 A♭7 G7 D♭7 Cm
Don't you know that you're toxic?

Verse 2

Cm
It's getting late to give you up,
E♭7
I took a sip from the devil's cup,
G7 Cm
Slowly it's taking over me.

Pre-chorus 2

Cm
Too high, can't come down,
E♭7 G7
It's in the air and it's all around,
Cm
Can you feel me now?

Chorus 2

Cm E♭7
With a taste of your lips I'm on a ride,
D7 D♭7
You're toxic, I'm slipping under.
Cm E♭7
With a taste of a poison paradise,
A♭7
I'm addicted to you,
G7 D♭7 Cm
Don't you know that you're toxic?
E♭7 D7
And I love what you do,
D♭7 Cm E♭7 A♭7
Don't you know that you're toxic?
G7
Don't you know that you're toxic?

```
Link        | Cm    | E♭7   | D7    | D♭7   |

            | Cm    | A♭7   | G7    | Cm    | Cm    ||


            Cm                                   E♭7  D7
Chorus 3    Taste of your lips I'm on a ride,
                           D♭7
            You're toxic, I'm slipping under.
                     Cm                 E♭7
            With a taste of a poison paradise,
                A♭7
            I'm addicted to you,
                        G7                  D♭7    Cm
            Don't you know that you're toxic?
                                                E♭7
            With a taste of your lips I'm on a ride,
            D7                       D♭7
               You're toxic, I'm slipping under.
                     Cm                 E♭7
            With a taste of a poison paradise,
                A♭7
            I'm addicted to you,
                        G7                  D♭7    Cm
            Don't you know that you're toxic?


            Cm                    E♭7                       D7
Outro       Intoxicate me now     with your loving now,
                                   D♭7
            I think I'm ready now,     I think I'm ready now.
            Cm                        E♭7                       A♭7
               Intoxicate me now      with your loving now,
                                        N.C.  (Cm)
            I think I'm ready now.
```

Uptown Girl

Words & Music by Billy Joel

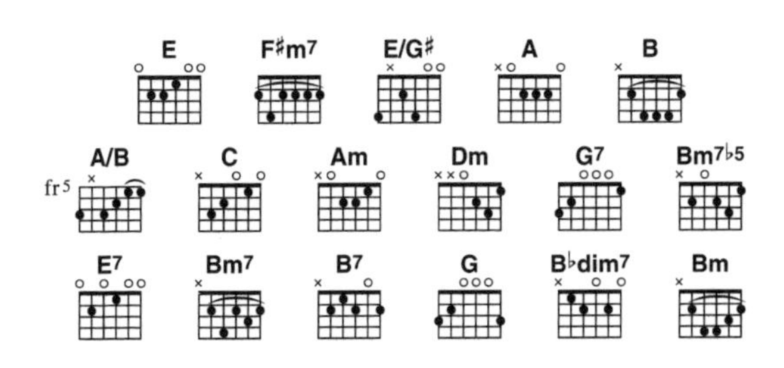


```
             E                F♯m7          E/G♯
*Intro*        Oh, oh, oh, oh, oh, oh, oh, oh.
                         A      B
             Oh, oh, oh, oh, oh, oh, oh.

             E
*Verse 1*    Uptown girl,
             F♯m7                       E/G♯
               She's been living in her uptown world.
             A            A/B        E
               I bet she's never had a backstreet guy,
             F♯m7                    E/G♯
               I bet her mama never told her why.
             A            B
               I'm gonna try for an...

             E
*Verse 2*    Uptown girl,
             F♯m7                       E/G♯
               She's been living in her white bread world,
             A           B           E
               As long as anyone with hot blood can.
             F♯m7                              E/G♯
               And now she's looking for a downtown man,
             A              B
              That's what I am.
```

Bridge 1

C Am Dm G7
And when she knows what she wants from her time.

C Am Bm7♭5 E7
And when she wakes up and makes up her mind.

A F♯m7 Bm7
She'll see I'm not so tough just because

B7
I'm in love with an...

Verse 3

E
Uptown girl.

F♯m7 E/G♯
You know I've seen her in her uptown world.

A B E
She's getting tired of her high class toys

F♯m7 E/G♯
And all her presents from her uptown boys,

A B
She's got a choice.

Interlude 1

G A B♭dim7 Bm A
Oh, oh, oh, oh, oh, oh, oh, oh, oh, oh, oh, oh, oh, oh, oh.

G A B♭dim7 B7
Oh, oh, oh, oh, oh, oh, oh, oh, oh, oh, oh, oh, oh, oh.

Verse 4

E
Uptown girl,

F♯m7 E/G♯
You know I can't afford to buy her pearls,

A B E
But maybe someday when my ship comes in

F♯m7 E/G♯
She'll understand what kind of guy I've been

A B
And then I'll win.

Bridge 2

```
C                     Am            Dm        G7
   And when she's walking, she's looking so fine
C                     Am           Bm7♭5        E7
   And when she's talking she'll say that she's mine.
A                   F♯m7         Bm7
   She'll say I'm not so tough just because
B7
   I'm in love with an...
```

Verse 5 As Verse 2

Interlude 2 As Interlude 1

Outro

```
E
Uptown girl,
F♯m7                   E/G♯
   She's my uptown girl.
     A             B
You know I'm in love with an
   E
‖: Uptown girl,
F♯m7            E/G♯
   My uptown girl.
     A             B
You know I'm in love with an... :‖  Repeat to fade
```

Three Times A Lady

Words & Music by Lionel Richie

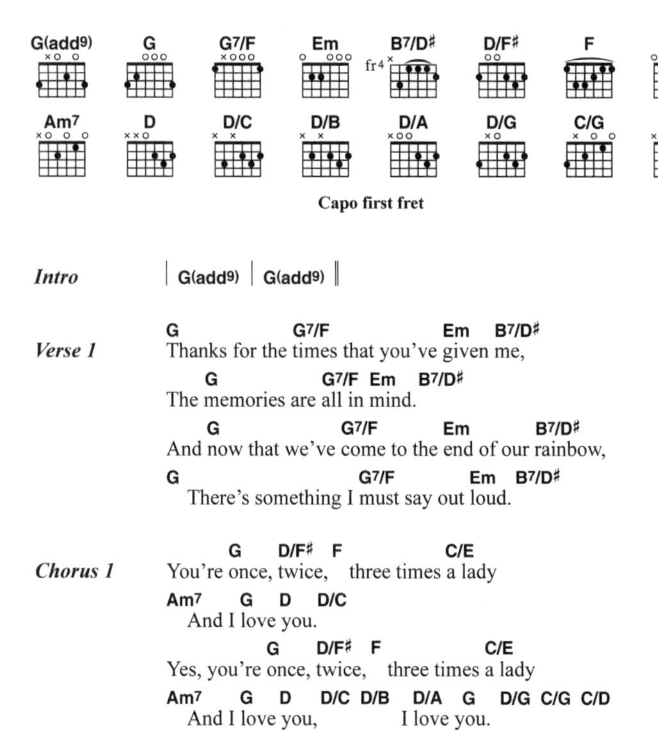

Capo first fret

Intro | G(add9) | G(add9) ||

Verse 1

G G7/F Em B7/D♯
Thanks for the times that you've given me,
G G7/F Em B7/D♯
The memories are all in mind.
G G7/F Em B7/D♯
And now that we've come to the end of our rainbow,
G G7/F Em B7/D♯
There's something I must say out loud.

Chorus 1

G D/F♯ F C/E
You're once, twice, three times a lady
Am7 G D D/C
And I love you.
G D/F♯ F C/E
Yes, you're once, twice, three times a lady
Am7 G D D/C D/B D/A G D/G C/G C/D
And I love you, I love you.

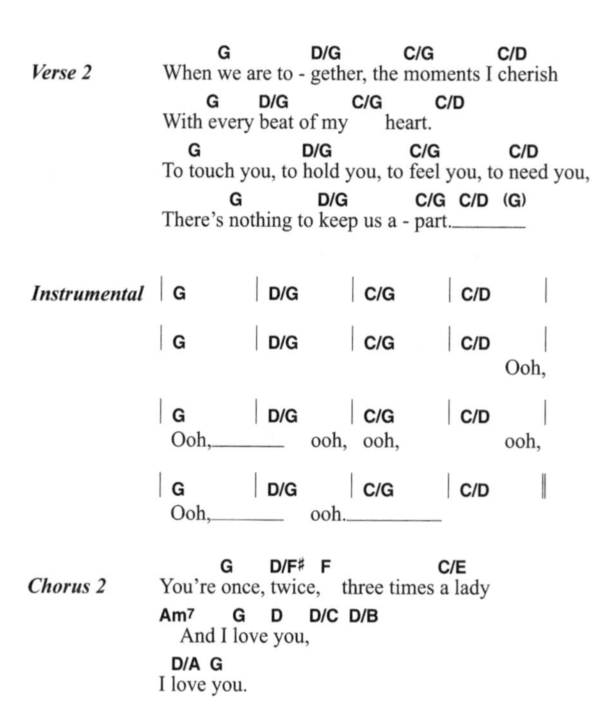
Verse 2
G D/G C/G C/D
When we are to - gether, the moments I cherish
G D/G C/G C/D
With every beat of my heart.
G D/G C/G C/D
To touch you, to hold you, to feel you, to need you,
G D/G C/G C/D (G)
There's nothing to keep us a - part.
Instrumental
| G | D/G | C/G | C/D |
| G | D/G | C/G | C/D |
Ooh,
| G | D/G | C/G | C/D |
Ooh, ooh, ooh, ooh,
| G | D/G | C/G | C/D ||
Ooh, ooh.
Chorus 2
G D/F♯ F C/E
You're once, twice, three times a lady
Am7 G D D/C D/B
And I love you,
D/A G
I love you.

Virtual Insanity

Words & Music by Jason Kay and Toby Smith

E♭m7 (fr6) A♭7 (fr4) D♭7 (fr4) G♭maj7 Cm7♭5 (fr7) Bmaj7 (fr7) B♭7aug (fr6) A♭m7 (fr4)

D♭m7 (fr4) Amaj7 (fr5) G♭m7 A♭7aug (fr4) Ddim7 (fr4) D♭6/F (fr6) G♭7sus4 G♭7

Intro

E♭m7 A♭7 D♭7 G♭maj7 Cm7♭5
Ooh, hey, hey, oh, what we're living in,

Bmaj7 B♭7aug
Let me tell ya.

Verse 1

(B♭7aug) E♭m7 A♭7
And it's a wonder man can eat at all

D♭7 G♭maj7
When things are big that should be small.

Cm7♭5 Bmaj7 B♭7aug E♭m7
Who can tell what magic spells we'll be doing for us?

A♭7 D♭7 G♭maj7
And I'm giving all my love to this world only to be told

Cm7♭5 Bmaj7 B♭7aug E♭m7
I can't see, I can't breathe, no more will we be.

A♭7 D♭7
And nothing's going to change the way we live,

G♭maj7 Cm7♭5
'Cause we can always take but never give.

Bmaj7 B♭7aug
And now that things are changing for the worse,

E♭m A♭7
See, wha, it's a crazy world we're living in.

D♭7 G♭maj7 Cm7♭5 Bmaj7
And I just can't see that half of us immersed in sin

B♭7aug
Is all we have to give these…

Chorus 1

Bmaj7 B♭7aug E♭m7 A♭m7
Futures made of virtual in - sanity,

B♭7aug Bmaj7 B♭7aug E♭m7 A♭m7 B♭7aug
Now, always seem to be governed by this love we have

Bmaj7 B♭7aug E♭m7 A♭m7
For useless, twisting, our new tech - nology,

B♭7aug Bmaj7 B♭7aug E♭m7 A♭m7 B♭7aug
Oh, now there is no sound, for we all live under - ground.

Verse 2

(B♭7aug) E♭m7 A♭7
And I'm thinking what a mess we're in,

D♭7 G♭maj7
Hard to know where to begin.

Cm7♭5 Bmaj7 B♭7aug E♭m7
If I could slip the sickly ties that earthly man has made

A♭7 D♭7 G♭maj7 Cm7♭5
And now every mother can choose the colour

Bmaj7 B♭7aug E♭m7
Of her child that's not nature's way.

A♭7 D♭7
Well that's what they said yester - day,

G♭maj7 Cm7♭5
There's nothing left to do but pray.

Bmaj7 B♭7aug
I think it's time I found a new religion.

E♭m A♭7 D♭7 G♭maj7
Whoa, it's so insane to synthesize an - other strain,

Cm7♭5 Bmaj7 B♭7aug
There's something in these futures that we have to be told.

Chorus 2 As Chorus 1

Chorus 3

Bmaj7 B♭7aug E♭m7 A♭m7 B♭7aug
Now there is no sound, if we all live underground.

Bmaj7 B♭7aug E♭m7 A♭m7 B♭7aug
And now it's virtual insanity, forget your virtual re - ality.

Bmaj7 B♭7aug E♭m7 A♭m7 B♭7aug Bmaj7
Oh, there's nothing so bad___ as a mad happy man.

B♭7aug E♭m7 A♭m7 B♭7aug
Oh yeah, I know yeah, take it to the bridge.

Bridge 1

| E♭m7 | E♭m7 | B♭7 | B♭7 |

| Bmaj7 | Bmaj7 | A♭m7 | B♭7aug |
Ooh,

E♭m7 B♭7
Oh, no one can go on.

| Bmaj7 | Bmaj7 | A♭m7 | B♭7aug |

| E♭m7 | E♭m7 | B♭7 | B♭7 |

| Bmaj7 | Bmaj7 | A♭m7 | B♭7 ||

Bridge 2

D♭m7 A♭7 Amaj7
Of this virtual insanity we're living in

G♭m7 A♭7aug
Has got to change, yeah.

D♭m7 A♭7
Things will never be the same

Amaj7
And it can't go on while we're living in

G♭m7 A♭7aug
Oh, oh virtual insanity.

E♭m7 B♭7
Oh, this world, has got to change,

Bmaj7 A♭m7 B♭7aug
'Cause I just, I just can't keep going on

E♭m7 B♭7
It was virtual, virtu - al insanity

Bmaj7 A♭m7 B♭7aug
That we're living in, that we're living in,

A♭m7 B♭7aug (E♭m7)
That virtual in - sanity is what it is.

Link

| E♭m7 | A♭7 | D♭7 | G♭maj7 |
Yeah, ooh.

| Cm7♭5 | Bmaj7 | B♭7aug |

| E♭m7 | A♭7 | D♭7 | G♭maj7 |

| Cm7♭5 | Bmaj7 | B♭7aug ||

Chorus 4 As Chorus 1

Chorus 5 As Chorus 1

```
              Bmaj7        B♭7aug  E♭m7        A♭m7    B♭7aug
Chorus 6        Living in          virtual in - sanity.
(ad lib.)     Bmaj7        B♭7aug  E♭m7        A♭m7    B♭7aug
                Living in          virtual in - sanity.
              Bmaj7        B♭7aug  E♭m7        A♭m7    B♭7aug
                Living in          virtual in - sanity.
              Bmaj7        B♭7aug  E♭m7        A♭m7    B♭7aug
                Living in          virtual in - sanity.

              Bmaj7 Ddim7 E♭m7         D♭6/F    G♭7sus4  G♭7              Bmaj7
Outro                     Virtual in - sanity is what    we're living in.
              Cm7♭5       Bmaj7 B♭7aug
                   Yeah,___       the world is all right.
```

Walk On The Wild Side

Words & Music by Lou Reed

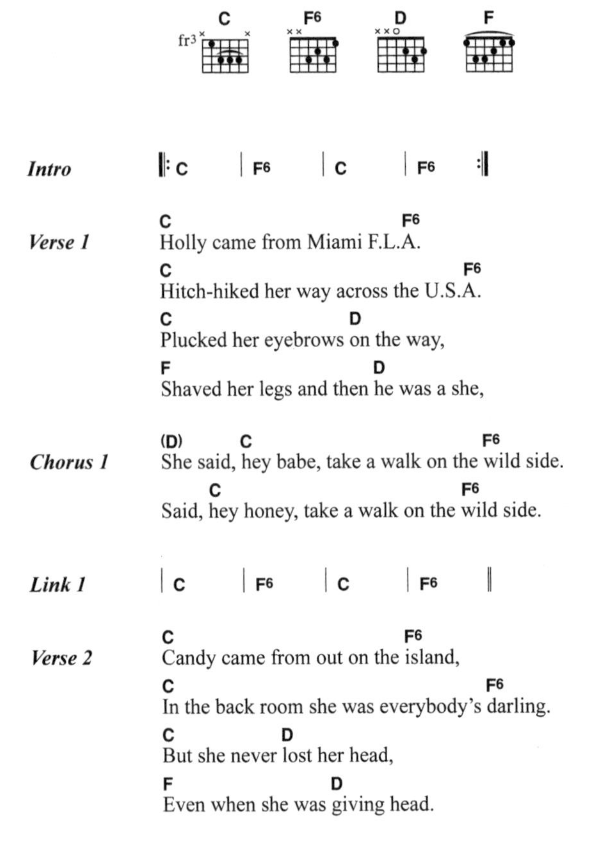

Intro | : C | F6 | C | F6 : |

Verse 1

```
C                                F6
Holly came from Miami F.L.A.
C                                        F6
Hitch-hiked her way across the U.S.A.
C                        D
Plucked her eyebrows on the way,
F                           D
Shaved her legs and then he was a she,
```

Chorus 1

```
(D)     C                               F6
She said, hey babe, take a walk on the wild side.
      C                                F6
Said, hey honey, take a walk on the wild side.
```

Link 1 | C | F6 | C | F6 ||

Verse 2

```
C                                F6
Candy came from out on the island,
C                                          F6
In the back room she was everybody's darling.
C              D
But she never lost her head,
F                   D
Even when she was giving head.
```

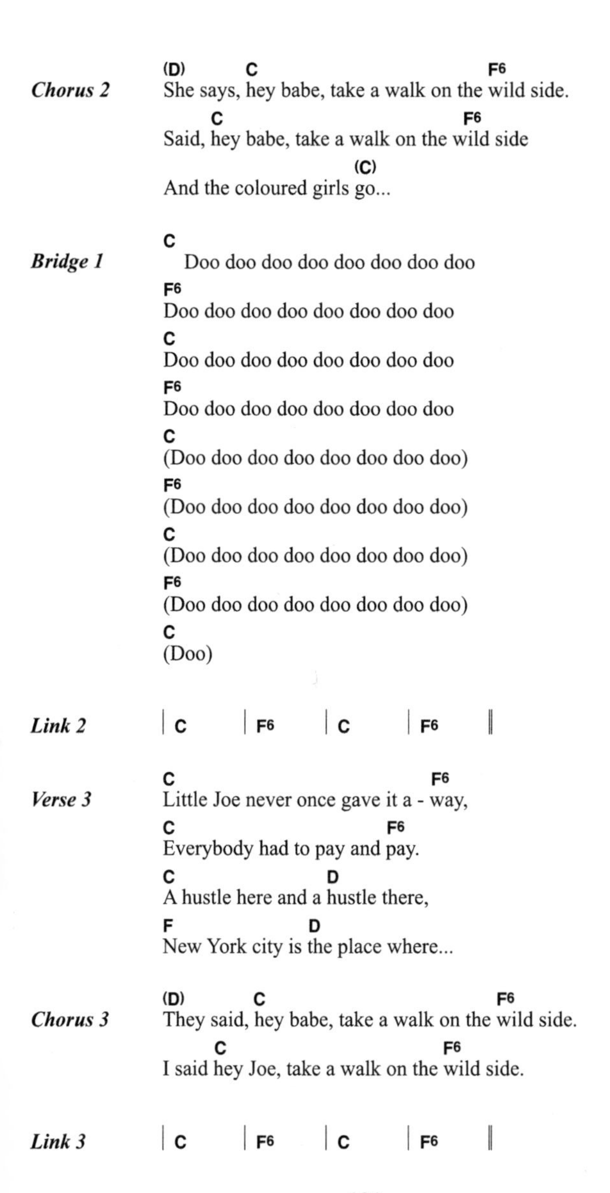

Chorus 2

(D) C F6
She says, hey babe, take a walk on the wild side.

C F6
Said, hey babe, take a walk on the wild side

(C)
And the coloured girls go...

Bridge 1

C
Doo doo doo doo doo doo doo doo

F6
Doo doo doo doo doo doo doo doo

C
Doo doo doo doo doo doo doo doo

F6
Doo doo doo doo doo doo doo doo

C
(Doo doo doo doo doo doo doo doo)

F6
(Doo doo doo doo doo doo doo doo)

C
(Doo doo doo doo doo doo doo doo)

F6
(Doo doo doo doo doo doo doo doo)

C
(Doo)

Link 2

| C | F6 | C | F6 ‖

Verse 3

C F6
Little Joe never once gave it a - way,

C F6
Everybody had to pay and pay.

C D
A hustle here and a hustle there,

F D
New York city is the place where...

Chorus 3

(D) C F6
They said, hey babe, take a walk on the wild side.

C F6
I said hey Joe, take a walk on the wild side.

Link 3

| C | F6 | C | F6 ‖

Verse 4

```
C                                    F6
Sugar Plum Fairy came and hit the streets,
C                                      F6
Looking for soul food and a place to eat.
C          D
Went to the Apollo,
    F                        D
You should have seen him go, go, go.
```

Chorus 4

```
(D)       C                                  F6
They said, hey Sugar, take a walk on the wild side.
      C                                F6
I said, hey babe, take a walk on the wild side.

All right.
```

Link 4

```
| C        | F6       | C        | F6       ||
   Huh.
```

Verse 5

```
C                          F6
Jackie is just speeding a - way,
C                                   F6
Thought she was James Dean for a day.
C                D
Then I guess she had to crash,
    F               D
Valium would have helped that bash.
```

Chorus 5

```
(D)        C                              F6
She said, hey babe, take a walk on the wild side.
      C                                   F6
I said, hey honey, take a walk on the wild side.

And the coloured girls say...
```

Bridge 2

C
Doo doo doo doo doo doo doo doo
F6
Doo doo doo doo doo doo doo doo
C
Doo doo doo doo doo doo doo doo
F6
Doo doo doo doo doo doo doo doo
C
(Doo doo doo doo doo doo doo doo)
F6
(Doo doo doo doo doo doo doo doo)
C
(Doo doo doo doo doo doo doo doo)
F6
(Doo doo doo doo doo doo doo doo)
C
(Doo doo doo doo doo doo doo doo)
F6
(Doo doo doo doo doo doo doo doo)
C
(Doo doo doo doo doo doo doo doo)
F6
(Doo doo doo doo doo doo doo doo)
C
(Doo)

Outro

Sax. solo
‖: C | F6 | C | F6 :‖ *Repeat to fade*

What Becomes Of The Brokenhearted?

Words & Music by James A. Dean, Paul Riser & William Henry Weatherspoon

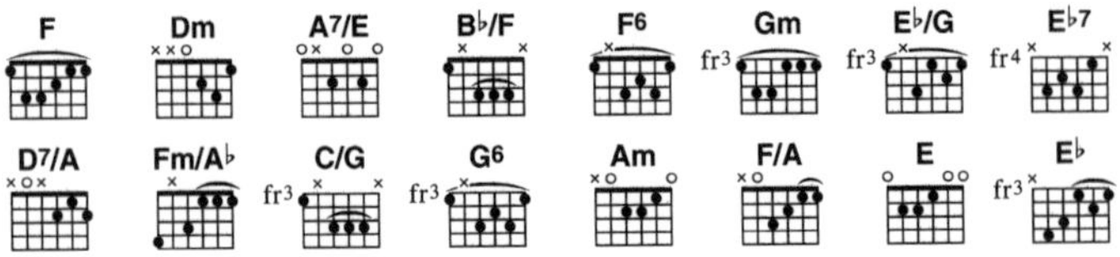

F Dm A7/E B♭/F F6 Gm E♭/G E♭7
D7/A Fm/A♭ C/G G6 Am F/A E E♭

Intro | F | F | F Dm A7/E |
| B♭/F | F6 | Gm | E♭/G |
| B♭/F | A7/E | E♭7 | E♭7 Dm A7/E ||

Verse 1
B♭/F F6
As I walk this land of broken dreams,
Gm E♭/G
I have visions of many things.
B♭/F F6
But happiness is just an illusion
Gm D7/A Fm/A♭
Filled with sadness and con - fusion.

Chorus 1
C/G G6
What becomes of the brokenhearted
Am F/A
Who had love that's now departed?
C/G
I know I've got to find
Am C/G E F Gm E♭
Some kind of peace of mind, baby.

Verse 2
B♭/F F6
The roots of love grow all around,
Gm E♭/G
But for me they come a - tumbling down.
B♭/F A7/E
Every day heartaches grow a little stronger,
E♭7 Dm A7/E
I can't stand this pain much longer.

Verse 3

B♭/F   F6
   I walk in shadows searching for light,
Gm   E♭/G
   Cold and alone, no comfort in sight.
B♭/F   F6
   Hoping and praying for someone who'll care,
Gm   D7/A   Fm/A♭
   Always moving and going no - where.

Chorus 2

C/G   G6
   What becomes of the brokenhearted
Am   F/A
   Who had love that's now departed?
C/G
I know I've got to find
Am   C/G   E   F   Gm E♭
Some kind of peace of mind, help me, please.

Verse 4

B♭/F   F6
   I'm searching though I don't succeed,
Gm   E♭/G
   But someone look, there's a growing need.
B♭/F   A7/E
   All is lost, there's no place for beginning,
E♭7   Dm A7/E
   All that's left is an unhappy ending.

Outro

B♭/F   F6
   Now what becomes of the brokenhearted
Gm   E♭/G
   Who had love that's now departed?
B♭/F   F6
I know I've got to find some kind of peace of mind.
Gm   E♭/G
I'll be searching everywhere just to find someone to care.
B♭/F   F6
I'll be looking every day, I know I'm gonna find a way.
Gm   E♭/G
Nothing's gonna stop me now.   *To fade*

Would I Lie To You?

Words & Music by Peter Vale & Mick Leeson

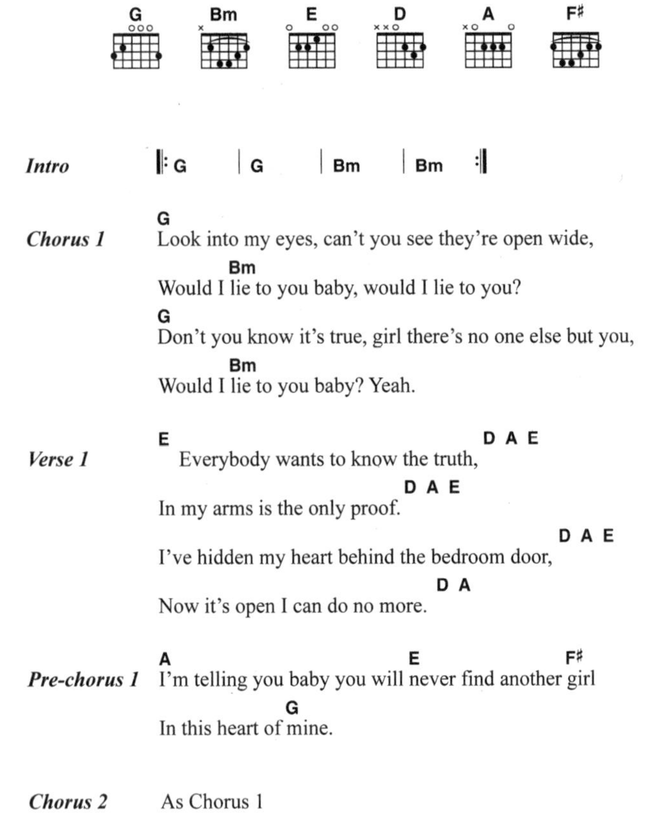

Intro | 𝄆 G | G | Bm | Bm 𝄇

Chorus 1

G
Look into my eyes, can't you see they're open wide,
Bm
Would I lie to you baby, would I lie to you?
G
Don't you know it's true, girl there's no one else but you,
Bm
Would I lie to you baby? Yeah.

Verse 1

E   D A E
Everybody wants to know the truth,
                                        D A E
In my arms is the only proof.
                                                          D A E
I've hidden my heart behind the bedroom door,
                                             D A
Now it's open I can do no more.

Pre-chorus 1

A   E   F♯
I'm telling you baby you will never find another girl
                G
In this heart of mine.

Chorus 2 As Chorus 1

Verse 2

E D A E
Everybody's got their history,
D A E
On every page a mystery.
D A E
You can read my diary, you're in every line,
D A
Jealous minds, never satisfied.

Pre-chorus 2 As Pre-chorus 1

Chorus 3 As Chorus 1

Bridge

(G) N.C.(E)
(Would I lie to you)
When you wanna see me night and day.
(Would I lie to you)
If I tell you that I'm here to stay.
(Would I lie to you)
Do you think I give my love away?
(Would I lie)
That's not the kind of game I play.

Pre-chorus 3

A E F♯
I'm telling you baby you will never find another girl
G
In this heart of mine.
In this heart of mine, deep in my heart.

Chorus 4

G
𝄆 Look into my eyes, can't you see they're open wide,
Bm
Would I lie to you baby, would I lie to you?
G
Don't you know it's true, girl there's no one else but you,
Bm
Would I lie to you baby? Yeah. 𝄇 *Repeat ad lib. to fade*

Wuthering Heights

Words & Music by Kate Bush

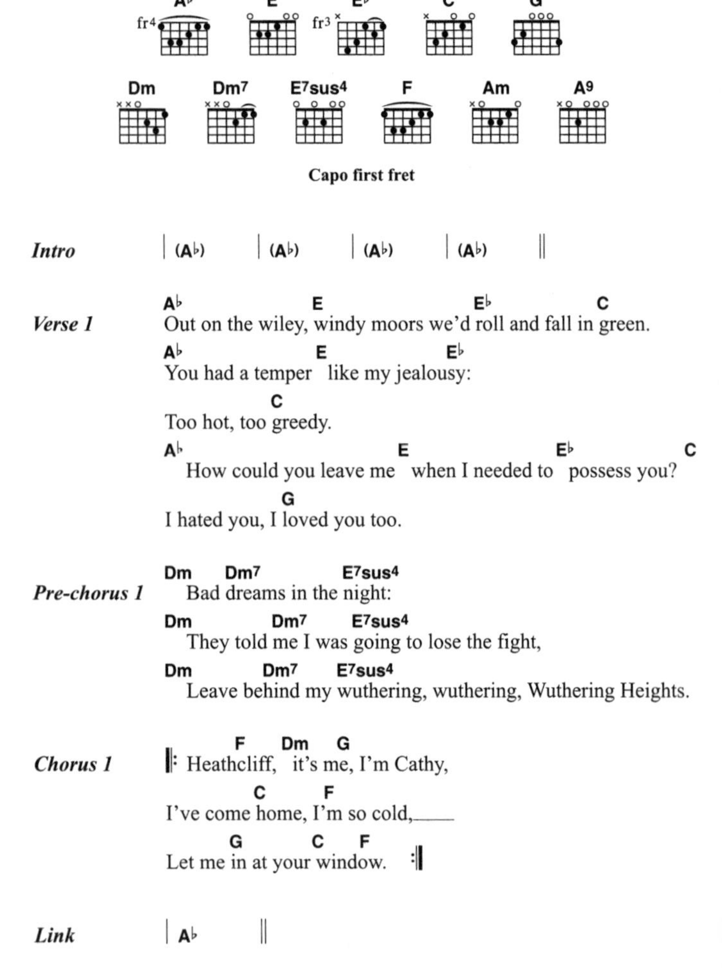

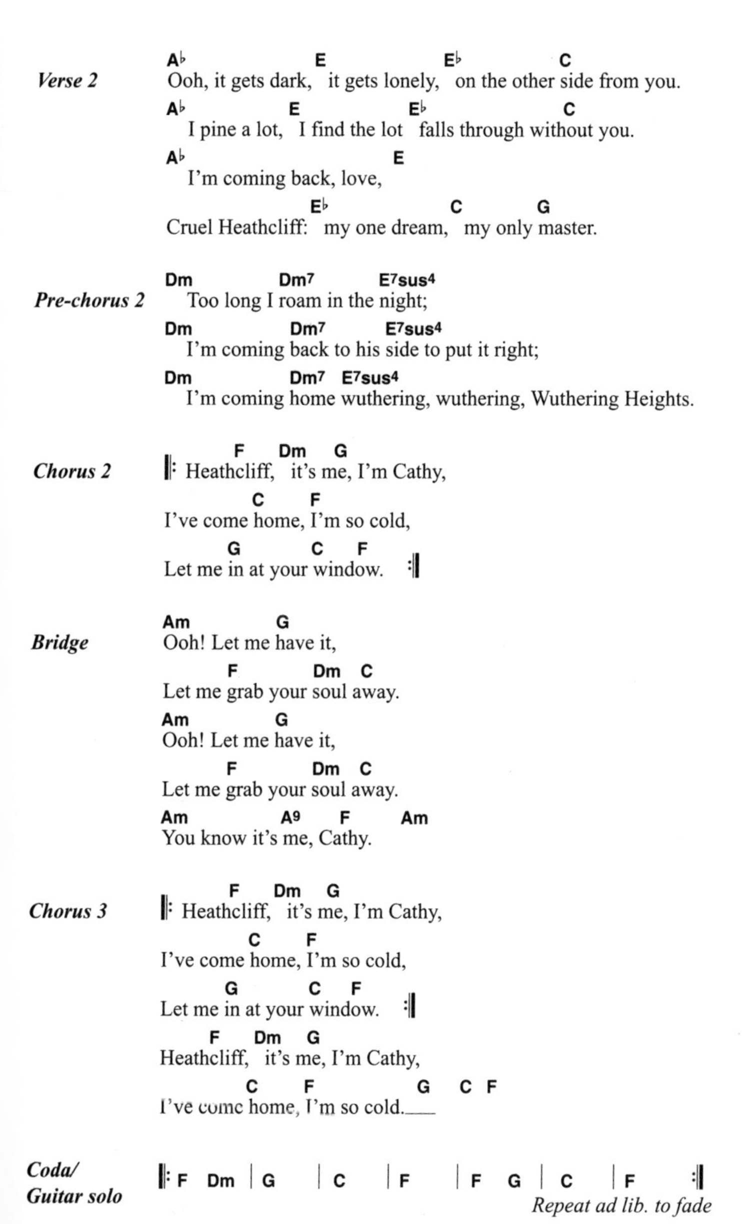

Verse 2

A♭ E E♭ C
Ooh, it gets dark, it gets lonely, on the other side from you.
A♭ E E♭ C
I pine a lot, I find the lot falls through without you.
A♭ E
I'm coming back, love,
E♭ C G
Cruel Heathcliff: my one dream, my only master.

Pre-chorus 2

Dm Dm7 E7sus4
Too long I roam in the night;
Dm Dm7 E7sus4
I'm coming back to his side to put it right;
Dm Dm7 E7sus4
I'm coming home wuthering, wuthering, Wuthering Heights.

Chorus 2

F Dm G
‖: Heathcliff, it's me, I'm Cathy,
C F
I've come home, I'm so cold,
G C F
Let me in at your window. :‖

Bridge

Am G
Ooh! Let me have it,
F Dm C
Let me grab your soul away.
Am G
Ooh! Let me have it,
F Dm C
Let me grab your soul away.
Am A9 F Am
You know it's me, Cathy.

Chorus 3

F Dm G
‖: Heathcliff, it's me, I'm Cathy,
C F
I've come home, I'm so cold,
G C F
Let me in at your window. :‖
F Dm G
Heathcliff, it's me, I'm Cathy,
C F G C F
I've come home, I'm so cold.___

Coda/ Guitar solo

‖: F Dm | G | C | F | F G | C | F :‖

Repeat ad lib. to fade

Young Folks

Words & Music by Peter Morén, John Eriksson & Björn Yttling

F Dm C Am

Intro

|: F | Dm | C | Am |
| F | Dm | Am | Am :|

Verse 1

```
F                        Dm          C                        Am
If I told you things I did before, told you how I used to be,
F                             Dm          Am
Would you go along with someone like me?
F                         Dm               C                    Am
If you knew my story word for word, had all of my histo - ry,
F                             Dm          Am
Would you go along with someone like me?
```

Verse 2

```
(C)       F                   Dm               C              Am
I did be - fore and had my share, it didn't lead nowhere,
F                        Dm            C    Am
I would go along with someone like you.
               F                 Dm                 C               Am
It doesn't matter what you did, who you were hanging with,
F                              Dm          Am
We could stick around and see this night through.
```

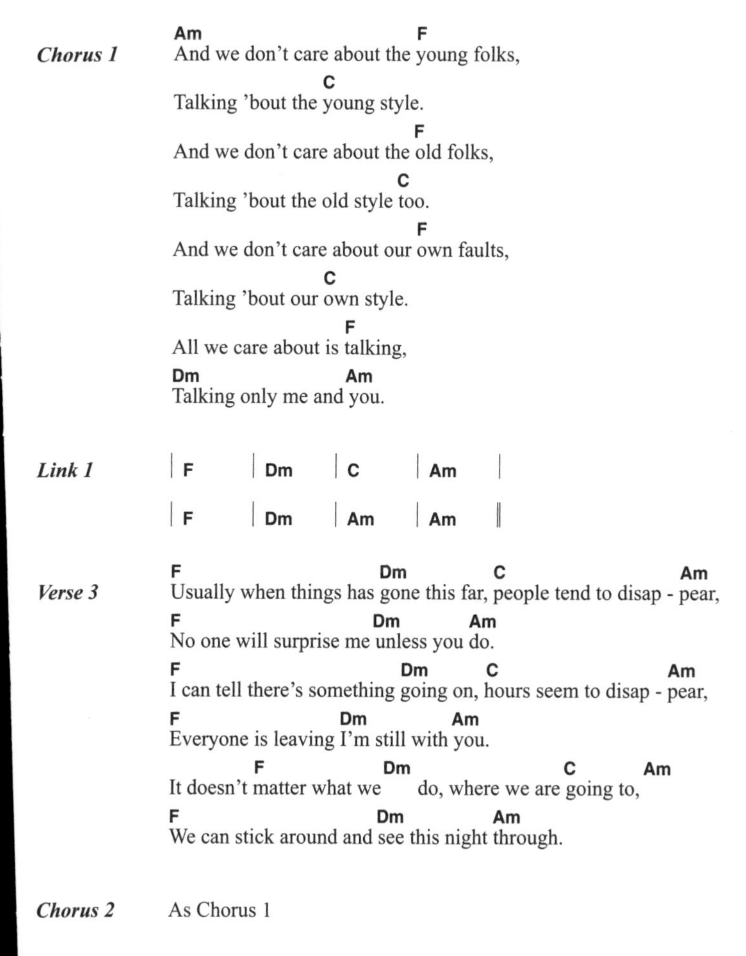

Chorus 1

Am F
And we don't care about the young folks,
C
Talking 'bout the young style.
F
And we don't care about the old folks,
C
Talking 'bout the old style too.
F
And we don't care about our own faults,
C
Talking 'bout our own style.
F
All we care about is talking,
Dm Am
Talking only me and you.

Link 1

| F | Dm | C | Am |
| F | Dm | Am | Am ||

Verse 3

F Dm C Am
Usually when things has gone this far, people tend to disap - pear,
F Dm Am
No one will surprise me unless you do.
F Dm C Am
I can tell there's something going on, hours seem to disap - pear,
F Dm Am
Everyone is leaving I'm still with you.
F Dm C Am
It doesn't matter what we do, where we are going to,
F Dm Am
We can stick around and see this night through.

Chorus 2

As Chorus 1

```
            Am                          F
Chorus 3    And we don't care about the young folks,
                           C
            Talking 'bout the young style.
                                        F
            And we don't care about the old folks,
                                      C
            Talking 'bout the old style too.
                                        F
            And we don't care about our own faults,
                           C
            Talking 'bout our own style.
                                  F
            All we care about is talking,
            Dm                 Am
            Talking only me and you.
                               (F)
            Talking only me and you.

Outro       | F     | Dm    | C     | Am    |

            | F     | Dm    | Am                    (F)
                                Talking only me and you.

            | F     | Dm    | C     | Am    |

            | F     | Dm    | Am                    (F)
                                Talking only me and you.

            | F     | Dm    | C     | Am    |

            | F     | Dm    | C     | Am    ||
```

1 2 3 4 5 6 7 8 9